INTERMEDIATE
LOGIC

*For Christian Private
and Home Schools*

James B. Nance

Canon Press
MOSCOW, IDAHO

The Mars Hill Textbook Series

Introductory Logic, Doug Wilson & James B. Nance
Introductory Logic: Video Tapes featuring James B. Nance
Introductory Logic: Teacher Training Video Tapes featuring James B. Nance

Intermediate Logic, James B. Nance
Intermediate Logic: Video Tapes featuring James B. Nance
Intermediate Logic: Teacher Training Video Tapes featuring James B. Nance

Latin Primer: Book I, Martha Wilson
Latin Primer I: Video Tapes featuring Julie Garfield
Latin Primer I: Audio Pronunciation Tape featuring Julie Garfield

Latin Primer: Book II, Martha Wilson
Latin Primer II: Video Tapes featuring Julie Garfield
Latin Primer II: Audio Pronunciation Tape featuring Julie Garfield

Latin Primer: Book III, Martha Wilson
Latin Primer III: Video Tapes featuring Julie Garfield
Latin Primer III: Audio Pronunciation Tape featuring Julie Garfield

Latin Grammar: Book I, Doug Wilson & Karen Craig
Latin Grammar: Book II, Karen Craig

Matin Latin Book I, Karen Craig
Matin Latin Flashcards Book I, Karen Craig
Matin Latin Worksheet Pkt. Book I, Karen Craig
Matin Latin I: Video Tapes featuring Karen Craig

Matin Latin Book II, Karen Craig
Matin Latin Flashcards Book II, Karen Craig
Matin Latin Worksheet Pkt. Book II, Karen Craig
Matin Latin II: Video Tapes featuring Karen Craig

James B. Nance, Intermediate Logic
©1996 by James B. Nance
Published by Canon Press, P.O. Box 8741, Moscow, ID 83843
800-488-2034 http://www.canonpress.org

First Edition 1996 (Rev. 2002)

Printed in the United States of America

ISBN: 1-885767-13-7

Table of Contents

Preface

Intermediate Logic is designed as a continuation to Introductory Logic by Douglas Wilson. Together, these two textbooks should provide sufficient material for a complete, first year course in elementary logic.

I have attempted to make this a useable workbook for the logic student. To that end I have included exercises for every lesson, which I have developed and used over the past four years of teaching logic. I have also made it my goal to write this text clearly and completely, such that an adult could teach himself the fundamentals of logic.

While writing Intermediate Logic I regularly consulted a number of other excellent logic textbooks. Most helpful has been Irving Copi's invaluable Introduction To Logic (Macmillan Publishing Co., 1978), which was the textbook for my first logic course at Washington State University. While doing my best to not lift material directly from it, that book has so shaped my own understanding of this subject that I undoubtedly echo much of its format and contents. I have also benefitted from The Art of Reasoning by David Kelley (W. W. Norton & Company, Inc., 1990) and The Logic Book by Bergmann, Moor and Nelson (McGraw-Hill, Inc., 1990).

I am indebted to many people for the completion of this project. I am thankful for the encouragement and example of my pastor, Doug Wilson, who helped me to understand the beauty and practicality of logic. I am also thankful for Chris Schlect, who has regularly spurred me on toward completing this book (though he undoubtedly would have written it quite differently) and has always encouraged me to think through my understanding of the subject. I am grateful for my illustrator and former logic student Paula Marston, who drew so many pictures on her assignments that I finally decided to employ her. The administrators of Logos School, Tom Garfield and Tom Spencer, have given me assistance and encouragement. My patient and ever-cheerful editor, Doug Jones, has always been there for me to bounce ideas off of. I owe special credit to my students throughout the years to whom I have had the true pleasure of introducing the world of logic. They have always forced me to re-evaluate my own understanding of the subject and have contributed more to this book than I or they realize.

Finally and most importantly I thank God for my lovely wife Giselle, who has proofread the text and worked through every lesson. To her this book is dedicated.

James B. Nance
January 1996

Introduction

Logic has been defined both as the *science* and the *art* of correct reasoning. People who study different sciences observe a variety of things: biologists observe living organisms, astronomers observe the heavens, and so on. From their observations they seek to discover natural laws by which God governs His creation. The person who studies logic as a science observes the mind as it reasons—as it draws conclusions from premises—and from those observations discovers laws of reasoning which God has placed in the minds of people. Specifically, he seeks to discover the principles or laws which may be used to distinguish good reasoning from poor reasoning. In deductive logic, good reasoning is *valid* reasoning—in which the conclusions follow necessarily from the premises. Logic as a science discovers the principles of valid and invalid reasoning.

Logic as an *art* provides the student of this art with practical skills to construct arguments correctly as he writes, discusses, debates, and communicates. As an art logic also provides him with rules to judge what is spoken or written, in order to determine the validity of what he hears and reads. Logic as a science discovers rules. Logic as an art teaches us to apply those rules.

Logic may also be considered as a symbolic language which represents the reasoning inherent in other languages. It does so by breaking the language of arguments down into symbolic form, simplifying them such that the arrangement of the language, and thus the reasoning within it, becomes apparent. The outside, extraneous parts of arguments are removed like a biology student in the dissection lab removes the skin, muscles and organs of a frog, revealing the skeleton of bare reasoning inside. Thus revealed, the logical structure of an argument can be examined, judged and, if need be, corrected, using the rules of logic.

So logic is a symbolic language into which arguments in other languages may be translated. Now arguments are made up of propositions, which in turn are made up of terms. In categorical logic, symbols (usually capital letters) are used to represent terms. Thus 'All men are sinners' is translated 'All M are S.' In propositional logic, the branch of logic with which this book primarily deals, letters are used to represent entire propositions. Other symbols are used to represent the logical operators which modify or relate those propositions. So the argument, 'If I don't eat, then I will be hungry; I am not hungry, so I must have eaten' may appear as $\sim E \supset H$, $\sim H$, E.

This book covers the translation and analysis of such propositions as they appear in arguments, with the primary concern of determining the validity of those arguments. Prior to this, however, is the important topic of defining terms.

DEFINITION

DEFINITION

The Purposes and Types of Definitions

A **definition** is a statement which gives the meaning of a term. A **term** is a concept with a precise meaning expressed by one or more words. A single term can be expressed by many different words. Words which are exact synonyms represent the same term. The English word *girl* and the Latin word *puella* represent the same term. Similarly, a single word can represent different terms. For example, the word *mad* can mean either angry or insane.

The ability to define terms accurately is a valuable skill. Lawyers must continually define their terms, and may use precise, technical language to do so. The same is true for teachers, scientists, philosophers, theologians, and most other professionals. To demonstrate the value of this skill, let us consider some of the purposes which definitions serve.

1. *To show relationships*

When terms are defined properly, the definition often gives some idea of the relationships which that term has with other terms. For example, if you were to define *man* as 'a rational animal,' your definition implies both that man has some relationship to other rational beings, such as angels and demons, and to other animals—bears, whales, and lizards. Or if *bald* is defined as 'having no hair,' its contradictory relationship with the term *hairy* is immediately apparent.

2. *To remove ambiguity*

Words are **ambiguous** when they have more than one possible meaning. Commonly, in a discussion or a debate, ambiguous words are used without the participants being aware of the ambiguity. The result is a verbal disagreement which may be cleared up by defining terms.

For instance, some people believe that Jesus' command to love your enemies is an absurd requirement because they are defining *love* to mean 'believe the other to be a nice person,' when in fact they know their enemies to be quite wicked and depraved. But biblically, *love* means 'to treat the other person lawfully from the heart,' which is to be our behavior toward all men. If this definition is made clear, the people may still think that the command is impossible, but at least they no longer should see it as absurd.

A definition which shows relationships or reduces ambiguity by providing a single, established meaning of a term is called a **lexical definition**.

11

3. *To reduce vagueness*

A problem similar to ambiguity is vagueness. A term is **vague** when its extent is unclear. The term itself may have a single, understood meaning, but there are 'gray areas' where it is uncertain if the given term applies. This is a common problem in descriptive terms, such as old, dark, tall, mature. If a father tells his children it must be warm outside before they can swim in the lake, the children often immediately want vagueness reduced: "*How* warm?" If the father responds, "At least eighty degrees Fahrenheit," the issue is made clear. Or if you are asked to give a small donation for a gift for the secretary, you may want a definition to reduce the vagueness of the term *small,* like, "By small I mean five dollars." This type of definition is a **precising definition**, because it seeks to make more precise what was previously vague or fuzzy.

4. *To increase vocabulary*

One of the most important elements of education is learning the meaning of unfamiliar terms. An increase in vocabulary means an increase in knowledge, which is why in English class students are taught "vocabulary words" and their definitions. In this very lesson you may have learned the definitions of terms like *ambiguity* and *vagueness.* Knowing these definitions helps us to make subtle distinctions and otherwise use language properly.

When a new word is invented, it is given a **stipulative definition**. Such definitions, if accepted, increase the vocabulary of the language to which they are added. New words are continually adopted into English, such as words resulting from new inventions (*laptop,* added in 1985), from sports (*screwball,* 1928), from other languages (*macho* from Spanish, also 1928), or coined out of someone's imagination (*boondoggle,* from an American scoutmaster in 1957).

5. *To explain theoretically*

Sometimes definitions are given for terms, not because the word itself is unfamiliar, but because the term is not understood. Such concepts require **theoretical definitions**, which are often scientific or philosophical in nature. For example, when your chemistry teacher defines water by its chemical formula H_2O, he is not trying to increase your vocabulary (you already knew the term *water*), but to explain its atomic structure.

Accepting a theoretical definition is like accepting a theory about the term being defined. If you define *spirit* as 'the life-giving principle of physical organisms,' you are inviting others to accept the idea that life is somehow a spiritual product.

6. *To influence attitudes*

Often terms are defined, not necessarily for the purpose of clarifying their meaning, but in order to influence the attitudes and emotions of an audience. *Abortion* has been defined as 'the slaughter of innocent children' on the one hand, 'the right of a woman to control her own body' on the other, or even the non-emotional 'termination of a pregnancy.' All these definitions aim at persuading the listener one way or another toward the term being defined, and as such are called **persuasive definitions**. Examples abound. Is democracy 'mob rule' or 'government by the people'? Is marriage 'the institutionalized slavery of women by men' or 'the blessed union of man and wife'? You can see the capacity of persuasive definitions for good or ill.

Summary: Definitions give meanings for terms. Definitions can show relationships between terms, remove ambiguity, reduce vagueness, increase vocabulary, explain theoretically, and influence attitudes. Along with these purposes are the five types of definitions: Lexical, precising, stipulative, theoretical, and persuasive.

Exercise One

1. Define *school* with the two types of definitions identified.

    PERSUASIVE: _____

    PRECISING: _____

2. Invent a new word and provide a definition for it.

    _____

    _____

    What type of definition is this? _____

3. Write an short, imaginary dialogue between two people having a verbal dispute. Then introduce a third person who settles the dispute by presenting to them lexical definitions for the word which eliminates the ambiguity.

Genus and Species

Terms are often defined by being placed among a higher category, or **genus**. The genus of a term is more general, broad, or abstract than the term itself. The term under a genus is called the **species**, which is a type, kind, or example of the term. The species is more specific, narrow, or concrete than the genus. Terms can be placed in a **genus and species hierarchy**, thus clearly showing the relationships between them. For example, consider the hierarchy below:

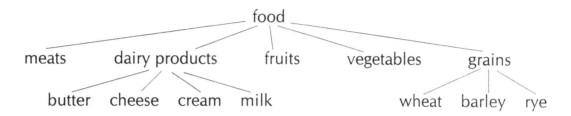

Here we see the genus *food*, and under it some of the species of the term food: meats, dairy products, fruits, vegetables, and grains. Of these, the terms *dairy products* and *grains* are shown to be genera (the plural of genus) for the species under them. The genus *dairy products* is broader than any of its species, such as butter, because dairy products includes not only butter but cheese, cream, milk, and any other species which could be placed under it. The chart also shows that the term *grains* is the genus of wheat, barley, and rye. Of course, many other terms could be included as species of grains. Can you think of any?

The words *genus* and *species* are relative terms. Each term can be both a genus and a species—a genus of the terms below it, and a species of the term above it. Thus *grains* is both a species of food and a genus of wheat. This process can continue (although not indefinitely) both downward and upward. *Cheese* could be the genus for different varieties of cheese, such as Swiss, Parmesan, and Cheddar. *Food* can be considered a species of *material* (if it is defined as 'edible material'), and so on.

One caution: do not confuse the genus and species hierarchies of logic with the similar hierarchy you may have learned in biology. In logic, there are no levels other than genus and species—no family, order, class, phylum, or kingdom.

Now look at the genus and species hierarchy for the term *sentence* on the next page.

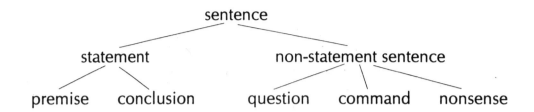

Two types of sentences are identified as species: sentences which are statements and sentences which are non-statements. These species are **mutually exclusive**—they do not overlap. No sentence is both a statement and a non-statement. They are also **exhaustive**; no other types of sentences exist. Theoretically, every genus can be divided into species which are both mutually exclusive and exhaustive. In practice, however, we rarely include every possible species under a genus. Are *questions, commands,* and *nonsense* an exhaustive list of sentences which are non-statements?

In the chart above, statements are divided into two types: premises and conclusions. The dividing principle here is 'How statements are used in arguments.' Other dividing principles could have been employed, such as: 'How the truth value of the statement is determined.' In that case, the species under *statement* would have been *self-supporting* (the truth value is determined solely by examining the statement itself) and *supported* (the truth value is determined by going outside of the statement), thus looking like this:

Finally, remember that a species is not a part of the genus, but rather a type or a kind of the genus. The species of the genus *bicycle* may include *mountain bike,* but not *handlebars.*

Summary: Terms can be placed in genus and species hierarchies. A genus is a category in which a term fits. A species is a type, kind, or example of a given term. Species should be mutually exclusive, and may be exhaustive.

Exercise Two

Explain the error or problem with each genus and species hierarchy shown.

1.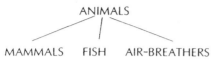

_____

_____

2.

_____

_____

3.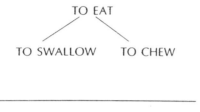

_____

_____

4.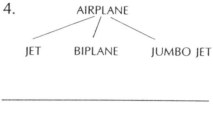

_____

_____

Fill in the genus and species hierarchy for each term given, identifying a) a genus for the term, b) another species under that genus, and c) a species of the term.

5.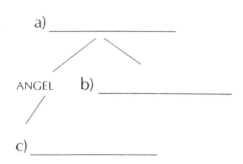

6.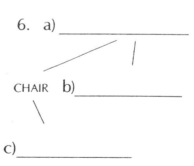

Extension and Intension

Two concepts closely associated with genus and species charts are extension and intension. The **extension** of a term is the sum of all the individual objects to which the term applies. Thus the extension of the term *book* is the set of all books—all novels, dictionaries, textbooks, manuals, etc. The extension of the term *helmet* would include every football helmet, bicycle helmet, space-suit helmet, and any other helmet imaginable.

All the objects included in the extension of a term have certain attributes in common. If they did not, we could not identify them with one term. The sum of the common attributes of a term is the **intension** of the term. Thus the intension of *book* would include attributes such as: having pages, on which words are written, which are bound together by some means. The intension of *helmet* would include these attributes: fitting on the head, resisting impact, made of protective material, and so on.

Extension and intension are inversely related. Given any genus and species chart, as you work your way up the chart, the extension of each term is greater than the previous terms, but the intension is smaller. Consider the hierarchy shown below:

The term *clock* has a greater extension than the term *digital clock*—that is, there are more clocks than there are digital clocks, because *clock* not only includes all digital clocks, but all other types of clocks as well. Similarly, there are more timepieces than there are clocks (can you name some?), so the extension of *timepiece* is greater than the extension of *clock*. As you go up a hierarchy, extension increases. However, intension *decreases* as you go up the chart, and increases as you go down. Timepieces have more attributes in common (i.e. a greater intension) than devices, clocks have more attributes in common than timepieces, and so on.

Increasing extension is parallel to increasing abstraction. The more abstract a term is, the greater its extent. *Device* is more abstract than *timepiece*. *To think* is more abstract than *to reason*, and thus would be higher on the genus and species chart, having a greater extension (though applying extension and intension to verbs tends to be more difficult than applying them to nouns).

Similarly, an increase in intension is accompanied by an increase in concreteness. The more attributes a term has, the more concrete it is. *Digital clock* is more concrete than *clock*, which is more concrete than *timepiece*.

The ability to list terms in order of increasing (or decreasing) extension (or intension) is a great help in making genus and species charts. Here we have in alphabetical order a number of terms from a genus and species hierarchy:

ANIMAL, APE, GORILLA, LIVING BEING, MAMMAL

Arranged in order of increasing extension (and decreasing intension), this list would look like this:

GORILLA, APE, MAMMAL, ANIMAL, LIVING BEING

Rearranged in order of increasing intension (that is, decreasing extension), the list would simply be placed in reverse order:

LIVING BEING, ANIMAL, MAMMAL, APE, GORILLA

Summary: The extension of a term is the sum of all the individual objects to which a term applies. The intension of a term is the sum of the common attributes of the term. Extension and intension are inversely related; as extension increases, intension decreases, and vice versa.

Exercise Three

1. Arrange in order of increasing extension:
    FIGURE, PLANE FIGURE, POLYGON, RECTANGLE, SQUARE

    _____

2. Arrange in order of decreasing extension:
    INSTRUMENT, SCIMITAR, CURVED SWORD, SWORD, WEAPON

    _____

3. Arrange in order of increasing intension:
    ANCIENT LANGUAGE, CLASSICAL LATIN, COMMUNICATION, LANGUAGE, LATIN

    _____

4. Arrange in order of decreasing intension:
    BAPTIST, CHRISTIAN, PROTESTANT, RELIGIOUS PERSON, SOUTHERN BAPTIST

    _____

5. Draw a genus and species hierarchy which includes the following terms:
    ALGEBRA, CHEMISTRY, SUBJECT, GEOMETRY, MATH, PHYSICS, SCIENCE

Methods of Defining

There are many methods of defining (giving the meaning of) a term. One of these methods, defining by genus and difference, directly relates to the genus and species hierarchies of the last two sections. Before we examine that method, however, we will consider two others which are commonly used.

1. *Defining by synonym*

When you look in the dictionary for the definition of a word, you often find a synonym (a word with the same meaning) of the word listed. This can be helpful, but only if you already understand the meaning of the synonym. For example, look up *progeny* and you will probably find that it is a synonym of *descendants* or *children*. This is helpful, since you know what these words mean. However, it may not help you to find out that *vicissitude* means *mutability*.

We all learned the meanings of words by this method when we were young. "Daddy, what's *essential* mean?" "Son, essential means necessary or important."

One limitation of defining by synonym is that many words do not have exact synonyms (indeed, some would argue that no two words mean *exactly* the same thing). For example, the word *oxygen* has no real synonym, and is best defined by some other method.

2. *Defining by example*

Another way children (and adults!) are taught the meanings of words is by being given examples of them. A child, upon asking her mother what money is, may be given a penny or shown a dollar bill. My children all learned the meaning of the word *cow* by having cows pointed out to them as we were driving by a field. "Jamie, look at all the cows!"

Similarly, words can be defined by example by using other words. We may define *noble gas* by listing helium, neon, argon, krypton, xenon and radon. This would be a complete definition. Often, representative samples can give partial (though adequate) definitions. Defining *sickness* by giving chicken pox and the flu as examples will probably meet the need.

This method also has some limitations. When a child is shown a typewriter and calls it a computer, he demonstrates the ambiguity of this method. When shown a computer, the child is uncertain as to what part is the meaning of the word 'computer'—the keyboard, the screen, or something else. The child may even think the act of pointing is the meaning of 'computer' because whenever he heard the word, that is what his father did. Despite this and similar problems, giving examples is a common means of defining.

3. *Defining by genus and difference*

This is the best method (though perhaps the most difficult) for defining words, not being subject to the limitations of defining by synonym or example. In this method, a term is defined by naming its genus, and then adding descriptive words which distinguish that term from every other species under that genus—that is, by providing the **difference**. For example, the term *backpack* may be defined as "a bag carried on the back." The genus is *bag*, the difference is *carried on the back*. The term *statement* has been defined as "a sentence which is true or false." The genus is *sentence*, the difference is *which is true or false*. This difference distinguishes statements from sentences which are *not* true or false, namely: questions, commands, and nonsense.

To choose a genus, try to determine what kind of thing the term is. What kind of thing is a computer? Is it a tool? a machine? a box? Also, remember that you are not defining words *per se*, which are often ambiguous, but you are defining *terms,* the concepts behind words. When defining *church,* for example, you need to determine if you are considering the body of believers or the building where they meet, before you develop a definition. When asked to define a term, only one definition is necessary.

When choosing the difference, remember that you are trying to distinguish the term from every other species under the genus. The difference should *exclude* species which the term does not *include,* and vice versa. Consider this definition of *battle:* 'a hostile encounter between two armies.' The difference 'between two armies' excludes battles between ships at sea, among other things, and is thus too narrow. Also note that the difference should be an essential one. A painting is not 'a picture drawn on canvas,' but 'a picture drawn by means of paint.'

The difference need not come after the genus. 'Three-sided polygon' is a good definition of *triangle* by method of genus and difference, even though the difference is given first.

You can see that this method of defining is particularly appropriate when the purpose is to show relationships between terms. The examples given in that section were examples of defining by genus and difference.

Summary: Terms may be defined by synonym, by example, or by genus and difference. Terms are defined by genus and difference by stating the genus of the term along with words distinguishing that term from every other species under the genus.

Exercise Four

Define the following terms by listing three examples of each.

1. NATION   2. BOARD GAME   3. CANDY

_____   _____   _____

_____   _____   _____

_____   _____   _____

Define these terms by identifying a synonym of each.

4. HAPPY   5. JOB   6. DINNER

_____   _____   _____

Define the following words by genus and difference.

7. BROTHER _____

8. DOE _____

9. WHISKER _____

10. QUEEN _____

Rules for Defining by Genus and Difference

1. *A definition should state the essential attributes of the term*

In any given term, there are some attributes which can be considered essential, and others which can be considered merely accidental or superficial. For example, an essential attribute of the term *oven* is its ability to heat. The fact that ovens are often shaped like a box is merely accidental, and thus this aspect should not be part of the definition of the term.

How can you tell the difference between essential and accidental attributes? For one thing, essential attributes tend to be the cause of accidental attributes. Consider the term *shin*. Which attribute is essential: 'located on the front of the leg below the knee,' or 'often injured in soccer games'? The former is the essential attribute, since it is one cause of the latter.

2. *A definition should not be circular*

This means that the word being defined should not be used as part of the definition. The difficulty this rule seeks to prevent is that circular definitions get you nowhere. If a student defines *logic* as 'the study of logic,' he hasn't really given the meaning at all.

This rule is not necessarily broken when part of a word is used in the definition. The definition of *polar bear* as 'a white bear which inhabits the arctic regions' is not circular, even though the word 'bear' appears in both parts.

This rule generally does not allow the use of synonyms. If synonyms are allowed, then define the word by synonym, not by genus and difference.

3. *A definition should not be too broad nor too narrow*

This rule is violated when a definition includes what it should exclude, or excludes what it should include. Consider this definition for the term *table*: 'a piece of furniture consisting of a flat slab of wood fixed on legs.' The problem is that this definition excludes tables made of metal or other material. Its extension is too small. A definition for table which *includes* too much is 'a piece of furniture with legs.' This would include chairs, couches, and other things which are not tables.

To check if the extensions of a term and its definition are equivalent, look for counter-examples. Is a *baby* a newborn person? What about a six-month old baby?

4. *A definition should not be unclear or figurative*

Definitions can be unclear for a variety of reasons. A definition may be unclear because it uses words which are ambiguous, vague, or obscure. If you define *bridge* as 'a structure which goes over an obstacle,' your definition is ambiguous. 'Goes over' has many meanings (can you think of some?), and the context is insufficient to make clear the meaning you want. A better definition would be 'a structure which is placed across an obstacle.' Defining *year* as 'a long period of time' breaks this rule, because the definition is vague. Defining *man* as 'an illative hominid' breaks this rule because 'illative' and 'hominid' are too obscure.

Definitions also may be unclear when the language of the definition is figurative or metaphorical. *"Ray:* a drop of golden sun" is a figurative definition. Such definitions may be poetic, but they often do not provide a clear meaning for the term.

5. *A definition should not be negative when it can be positive*

Sometimes when trying to define a term we are tempted to say what it *is not*, when we should say what it is. Such definitions by process of elimination break this rule. The term *magazine* should not be defined as 'a periodical which is not a newspaper.' To define an *isosceles triangle* as 'a triangle which is neither equilateral nor scalene' breaks this rule, even though the term and its definition have exactly the same extension.

Some terms are necessarily negative, such as *bald, empty,* and *penniless.* The definitions of these would be awkward if written positively, and thus they may be negative and not be exceptions to the rule.

6. *A definition should be of the same part of speech as the term*

If the term being defined is a noun, then the definition should be a noun. Similarly for the other main parts of speech: verbs, adjectives, and so on. This rule is broken, for example, when *to run* is defined as 'faster than a walk.' The term is a verb; the given definition is not.

A similar error occurs in this definition of *to run:* 'when you go faster than walking.' Is *to run* a time? Then don't use the word 'when.' Similar problems often crop up when the words *who, what, where, why* and *how* appear in definitions. These are best avoided, if possible.

Summary: When terms are defined by genus and difference, certain rules should be followed. A definition should 1) state the essential attributes of the term, 2) not be circular, 3) not be too broad or too narrow, 4) not be unclear or figurative, 5) not be negative when it can be positive, and 6) be of the same part of speech as the term.

Exercise Five

> ### A Definition Should:
> 1. State the essential attributes of the term
> 2. Not be circular
> 3. Not be too broad or too narrow
> 4. Not be unclear or figurative
> 5. Not be negative when it can be positive
> 6. Be of the same part of speech as the term

Identify the rule(s) broken by circling the correct number(s).

RULES BROKEN

1. *Mountain:* A natural object bigger than a hill.   1   2   3   4   5   6

2. *Wife:* Adam's rib.   1   2   3   4   5   6

3. *Brick:* Dried clay shaped into a brick.   1   2   3   4   5   6

4. *Rectangle:* The shape of a typical textbook.   1   2   3   4   5   6

5. *Headache:* When your head hurts.   1   2   3   4   5   6

6. *Capitalist:* A person who is not a socialist.   1   2   3   4   5   6

7. *To hate:* How you feel when you don't like something.   1   2   3   4   5   6

8. *Carpet:* Floor covering.   1   2   3   4   5   6

9. *To float:* To hover.   1   2   3   4   5   6

10. *Bag:* A pliant repository.   1   2   3   4   5   6

11. *Large:* Something that is not small.   1   2   3   4   5   6

12. *Life:* A roller coaster that we all ride.   1   2   3   4   5   6

Fill in the genus and species hierarchy for each term given, identifying a) a genus for the term, b) another species under that genus, and c) a species of the term.

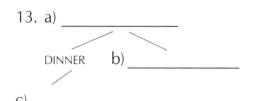

13. a) _____
    DINNER   b) _____
c) _____

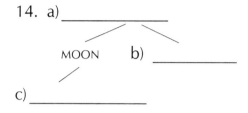

14. a) _____
    MOON   b) _____
c) _____

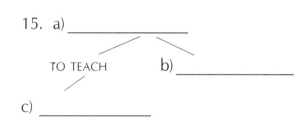

15. a) _____
    TO TEACH   b) _____
c) _____

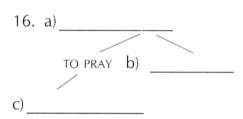

16. a) _____
    TO PRAY   b) _____
c) _____

Define the following terms by genus and difference, using the same genus from any corresponding terms in the charts above. Be careful not break any of the rules!

17. DINNER _____

18. MOON _____.

19. WRISTWATCH _____

20. BED _____

21. TO TEACH _____

22. TO PRAY _____

PROPOSITIONAL LOGIC

PROPOSITIONAL LOGIC

Introduction to Propositional Logic

Propositional logic is a branch of formal, deductive logic in which the basic unit of thought is the propositon, A **proposition** is a statement, a sentence which has a truth value. A single proposition can be expressed by many different sentences. The following sentences all represent the same proposition:

God loves the world.
The world is loved by God.
Mundum Deus amat.

These sentences represent the same proposition because they all have the same meaning.

In propositional logic, letters are used as symbols to represent propositions. Other symbols are used to represent words which modify or combine propositions. Because so many symbols are used, propositional logic has also been called 'symbolic logic.' The only propositions which are dealt with are **truth-functional** propositions. A proposition is truth-functional when the truth value of the proposition depends upon the truth value of its component parts. If it has only one component part, it is a **simple proposition**. A simple proposition is a categorical statement. The proposition 'God loves the world' is simple. If a proposition has more than one component part (or is modified in some other way), it is a **compound proposition**. Words which combine or modify simple propositions in order to form compound propositions (such as 'and' and 'or') are called **logical operators**.

For example, the proposition 'God loves the world and God sent His Son' is a truth functional, compound proposition. The word 'and' is the logical operator. It is truth functional because its truth value depends upon the truth value of the two simple propositions which make it up. Similarly, the proposition 'It is false that God loves the world' is compound, the phrase 'it is false that' being the logical operator. It is also truth functional, depending upon the truth value of the component 'God loves the world' for its total truth value. If 'God loves the world' is false, then the proposition 'It is false that God loves the world' is true, and vice versa.

However, the proposition 'Joe believes that God loves the world,' though compound (being modified by the phrase 'Joe believes that'), is *not* truth-functional, because its truth value does not depend upon the truth value of the component part 'God loves the world.' The proposition 'Joe believes that God loves the world' can be considered true, regardless of whether or not 'God loves the world' is true.

When a given proposition is analyzed as part of a compound proposition or argument, it is usually abbreviated by a capital letter, called a **propositional constant**. Propositional constants commonly have some connection with the propositions they symbolize, such as being the first letter of the first word, or some other distinctive word within the proposition. For example, the proposition 'The mouse ran up the clock' could be abbreviated M. On the other hand, 'The mouse did not run up the clock' may be abbreviated ~M (read as *not M*). Within one compound proposition or argument, the same propositional constant should be used to represent a given proposition. Note that a simple proposition cannot be represented by more than one variable.

When the *form* of a compound proposition or argument is being emphasized, logicians use **propositional variables**. It is customary to use lower case letters as propositional variables, starting with the letter *p* and continuing up the alphabet. A propositional variable could represent an unlimited number of propositions.

It is important to realize that a single constant or variable can represent not only a simple proposition but also a compound proposition. The variable *p* could represent 'God loves the world' or it could represent 'God loves the world but He hates sin.' The entire compound proposition 'It is false that if the mouse ran up the clock, then, if the clock did not strike one, then the mouse would not run down' could be abbreviated by a single constant **F**, or it could be represented by symbolizing each part, such as ~(M ⊃ (~S ⊃ ~D)). The decision concerning how to abbreviate a compound proposition depends on the purpose for abbreviating it. We will learn how to abbreviate compound propositions in the next few chapters.

Summary: A proposition is a statement. Propositions are truth-functional when the truth value of the proposition depends upon the truth value of its component parts. Propositions are either simple or compound. They are compound if they are modified or combined with other propositions by means of logical operators. Propositional constants are capital letters which represent a single proposition. Propositional variables are lower case letters which represent an unlimited number of propositions.

Exercise Six

What are two main differences between propositional constants and propositional variables?

1. _____

2. _____

Use the simple proposition 'We have seen God' to create the following:

3. A truth-functional compound proposition _____

   _____

4. A proposition which is *not* truth-functional _____

   _____

Circle S if the given proposition is simple. Circle C if it is compound.

5. The Lord will cause your enemies to be defeated before your eyes.
   S   C

6. There is a way that seems right to a man but in the end it leads to death.
   S   C

7. The fear of the Lord is the beginning of wisdom.
   S   C

8. If we confess our sins then He is faithful to forgive us our sins.
   S   C

9. It is false that a good tree bears bad fruit and a bad tree bears good fruit.
   S   C

10. The Kingdom of God is not a matter of talk but of power.
    S   C

Negation, Conjunction, and Disjunction

We will begin our study of abbreviating and analyzing compound propositions by learning about the three fundamental logical operators *negation, conjunction,* and *disjunction.* As we do, we will be answering three questions for each logical operator: what words in English are abbreviated by it, what is its symbol, and how is the truth value of the compound proposition affected by the truth values of the component parts.

Negation
Negation is the logical operator representing the words *not, it is false that,* or any other phrase which denies or contradicts the proposition. As we have already seen, the symbol " ~ " (called a *curl* or *tilde*) represents negation. If the proposition 'All roads lead to Rome' is represented by the propositional constant R, then ~ R means 'Not all roads lead to Rome' or 'It is false that all roads lead to Rome.' Note that the negation of a proposition is the contradiction of that proposition. Thus ~ R could also be translated 'Some roads do not lead to Rome.' If a proposition is true, its negation is false. If a proposition is false, its negation is true. This can be expressed by the following **truth table**, where T means *true* and F means *false*:

p	$\sim p$
T	F
F	T

Truth tables show how the truth value of a compound proposition is affected by the truth value of its component parts. The table above is called the **defining truth table** for negation.

Conjunction
When two propositions are joined by *and, but, still,* or other similar words, a conjunction is formed. The conjunction logical operator is symbolized by "•" (called, of course, a *dot*). If 'Main Street leads to home' is represented by the constant H, then 'All roads lead to Rome, but Main Street leads to home' could be represented by R • H (read as *R dot H* or *R and H*).

The conjunction is true if and only if the components (called **conjuncts**) are both true. If either conjunct is false, the conjunction as a whole is false.

The defining truth table for conjunction is therefore:

p	q	$p \bullet q$
T	T	T
T	F	F
F	T	F
F	F	F

Thus if 'All roads lead to Rome' is false and 'Main Street leads to home' is true, then the entire conjunction 'All roads lead to Rome but Main Street leads to home' is false, as seen on the third row down.

In ordinary English, the conjunction is not always placed between two distinct sentences. For example, 'Paul and Apollos were apostles' could be symbolized P • A, where P means 'Paul was an apostle' and A means 'Apollos was an apostle.' Similarly, the proposition 'Jesus is both God and Man' could be represented by G • M.

Disjunction

A disjunction is formed when two propositions are joined by the logical operator *or*, as in 'Paul was an apostle or Apollos was an apostle.' The symbol for disjunction is "v" (called a *vee*). The foregoing disjunction would thus be symbolized P v A (read simply *P or A*).

In English, the word *or* is ambiguous. In one sense it can mean 'this or that, but not both' (called the *exclusive or*). For example, in the sentence 'The senator is either a believer or an unbeliever,' the word or must be taken in the exclusive sense; nobody could be both a believer and an unbeliever at the same time in the same way. However, the word *or* can also mean 'this or that, or both' (called the *inclusive or*). This is how it should be taken in the sentence 'Discounts are given to senior citizens or war veterans,' since it is unlikely that a senior citizen who also happened to be a war veteran would not be allowed a discount.

In Latin, the ambiguity is taken care of by two separate words, *aut* meaning the exclusive or and *vel* meaning the inclusive or. Although it may seem like the exclusive sense of the word *or* is the more natural sense, in logic the disjunction is always taken in the inclusive sense. This is seen in the fact that the symbol v is derived from the Latin *vel*.

The defining truth table for disjunction is therefore:

p	*q*	*p* ∨ *q*
T	T	T
T	F	T
F	T	T
F	F	F

A disjunction is thus considered to be false if and only if both components (called **disjuncts**) are false. If either disjunct is true, the disjunction as a whole is true.

If the context of an argument requires that the word *or* be represented in the exclusive sense, as in 'The senator is either a republican or a democrat,' it may be translated with the more complicated (R ∨ D) • ~ (R • D). However, you should assume that *or* is meant in the more simple inclusive sense unless instructed otherwise.

As you see, logic may use parentheses in symbolizing complicated compound propositions. This is done to avoid ambiguity. The compound proposition A ∨ B • C could mean 'Either A or B, *and* C' or it could mean 'Either A, *or* B and C.' The ambiguity is removed in this proposition: (A ∨ B) • C, which represents the first option. The word 'both' is often an indicator of how parentheses are to be placed, as in the translation of the exclusive or in the previous paragraph, which could be read 'Either R or D, but not *both* R and D.' Also, it is usually improper to have three propositions in a row without two of them being set apart by parentheses.

When symbolizing compound propositions which include negation, it is standard practice to assume that whatever variable, constant or parenthesis the curl *immediately* proceeds is the one negated. For example, ~p ∨ q is equivalent to (~p) ∨ q. It is *not* equivalent to ~(p ∨ q). This helps prevent an excess of parentheses.

Summary: Three common logical operators are negation (*not*, symbolized ~), conjunction (*and*, symbolized •), and disjunction (*or*, symbolized ∨). These logical operators can be defined by means of truth tables. Negation reverses the truth value of a proposition, conjunction is true if and only if both conjuncts are true, and disjunction is false if and only if both disjuncts are false.

Exercise Seven

Given: **J** means *Joseph went to Egypt.*   **F** means *There was a famine.*

              I means *Israel went to Egypt.*   **S** means *The sons of Israel became slaves.*

Translate the following symbolic propositions.

1. F • I   _____

2. ~J v S   _____

Symbolize the following compound propositions.

3. Joseph and Israel went to Egypt.   _____

4. Israel did not go to Egypt.   _____

5. Israel went to Egypt but his sons became slaves.   _____

6. Either Joseph went to Egypt or there was a famine. _____

7. Joseph and Israel did not both go to Egypt.   _____

8. Neither Joseph nor Israel went to Egypt.   _____

9. Joseph and Israel went to Egypt; however, there was
    a famine and the sons of Israel became slaves.   _____

10. Israel went to Egypt; but either Joseph did not go to
    Egypt or there was a famine.   _____

Truth Tables for Determining Truth Values

So far we have seen that truth tables help define logical operators. Truth tables also serve other functions, one of which is to help us determine the truth value of compound propositions. The truth value of elementary negations, conjunctions and disjunctions can be immediately determined from their defining truth tables. But what about compound propositions like ~ p v (~ q • r)? To find the truth values for such complicated propositions, the following procedure may be followed:

1.   Draw a line, and on the leftmost part of the line place the variables (or constants) which are used in the proposition. Under these, put all the possible combinations of true and false. This will require four rows for two variables, eight rows for three variables, and in general 2^n rows for *n* variables. Under the first variable, place a T for each of the first half of the rows, then an F for each of the second half. Under the next variable, place half again as many Ts, half again as many Fs, then repeat this. The final column should have alternating single Ts and Fs, as follows:

p	q	r
T	T	T
T	T	F
T	F	T
T	F	F
F	T	T
F	T	F
F	F	T
F	F	F

You can verify for yourself that all the possible combinations of true and false are found in these eight rows.

2.   If any variables are negated, these should be added next, with the corresponding truth values under them, as shown:

			↓	↓	
p	q	r	~p	~q	
T	T	T	F	F	
T	T	F	F	F	
T	F	T	F	T	
T	F	F	F	T	
F	T	T	T	F	
F	T	F	T	F	
F	F	T	T	T	
F	F	F	T	T	

Whenever p is true, ~p is false, and vice versa, just as the defining truth table for negation shows. This is also the case for q and ~q.

3.   Continue to the next level of complexity in the proposition. As in mathematics, whatever is in parentheses should be completed before going outside the parentheses. In our example, the proposition in parentheses is ~q • r. This is placed on the line, and whenever both ~q and r are true, the conjunction ~q • r is true, according to the defining truth table for conjunction. Thus we now have:

				↓	↓
p	q	r	~p	~q	(~q • r)
T	T	T	F	F	F
T	T	F	F	F	F
T	F	T	F	T	T
T	F	F	F	T	F
F	T	T	T	F	F
F	T	F	T	F	F
F	F	T	T	T	T
F	F	F	T	T	F

4.   Continue with the same procedure, adding on to the truth table until the entire compound proposition is filled out. In our example, the propositions ~p and (~q • r) are disjuncts. Thus, whenever either is true, the whole disjunction

is true. We fill in those values and finish the truth table:

p	q	r	~p	~q	↓ (~q • r)	↓ ~p v (~q • r)
T	T	T	F	F	F	**F**
T	T	F	F	F	F	**F**
T	F	T	F	T	T	**T**
T	F	F	F	T	F	**F**
F	T	T	T	F	F	**T**
F	T	F	T	F	F	**T**
F	F	T	T	T	T	**T**
F	F	F	T	T	F	**T**

We see that whenever p, q and r are all true, the compound proposition ~p v (~q • r) is false, and so on down the truth table. As you get more familiar with this procedure, you will be able to dispense with the initial guide columns of true and false, working only with the compound proposition and placing the truth values directly beneath the variables in it.

Sometimes, the truth value of constants in a compound proposition are already known. In that case finding the truth value of the compound proposition requires only one row. For instance, assume that A is true, X and Y are false. Finding the truth value of (A v X) • ~Y requires this:

A	X	Y	(A v X)	~Y	(A v X) • ~Y
T	F	F	T	T	T

Summary: The truth values of a compound proposition may be determined by placing all possible combinations of true and false under the variables or constants, then using the definitions of the logical operators to determine the corresponding truth values of each component of the proposition.

Exercise Eight

Fill in the following truth table to determine the truth values for the exclusive or. The truth values for p and q are filled out for you on this first one.

p	q	(p v q)	(p • q)	~ (p • q)	(p v q) • ~ (p • q)
T	T				
T	F				
F	T				
F	F				

2. Determine the truth values for ~ (J • R) and ~ J • ~ R to prove that they are different. The initial J and R should follow the same pattern as p and q in problem one.

J	R	~ J	~ R	(J • R)	~ (J • R)	~ J • ~ R

3. Write sentences in English corresponding to the two compound propositions in problem two, using *Joe is a student* for J and *Rachel is a student* for R.

~ (J • R) _____

~ J • ~ R _____

Determine the truth value for each compound proposition. Assume that propositions A and B are true, X and Y are false. Circle T if the entire compound proposition is true. Circle F if it is false. Use the space at the right for showing any work.

4. ~A v B   T   F

5. X v ~B   T   F

6. ~(A v B)   T   F

7. (A • X) v (B • Y)   T   F

8. ~[X v (Y • ~A)]   T   F

Identify the truth value of each of the following sentences by circling T or F.

9. Jonah was a prophet or Isaiah was a prophet.
        T   F

10. Jeremiah was not a prophet but Isaiah was a prophet.
        T   F

11. It is not true that both Jeremiah was a prophet and Isaiah was not a prophet.
        T   F

12. Jonah was not a prophet or both Jeremiah and Isaiah were not prophets.
        T   F

13. A false proposition is not true.
        T   F

14. It is false that a true proposition is not false.
        T   F

15. It is true that it is false that a true proposition is not false.
        T   F

The Conditional

A very useful logical operator is the *conditional* (also called *hypothetical* or *material implication*). The conditional is an *if/then*-type proposition: 'If it is raining then I will take my umbrella.' The proposition following the *if* is called the **antecedent**, the proposition following the *then* is the **consequent**. In the preceding example, 'It is raining' is the antecedent; 'I will take my umbrella' is the consequent.

Conditionals can take many forms. All of the following propositions can be considered as conditionals, because they can all be translated into if/then form:

1. If I move my rook then he will put me in check.
2. The diode will light if the switch is flipped.
3. Fido is a dog implies that Fido is a mammal.
4. When you pray to the Lord he will heal you.
5. Cheating during a test is a sufficient condition for your suspension.

Can you determine the antecedent and the consequent for each of them?

The symbol for the conditional logical operator is "⊃" (called a *horseshoe*). 'If I move my rook then he will put me in check' could be symbolized R ⊃ C (read as *If R then C*).

In a conditional proposition, the antecedent is said to *imply* the consequent. That is, for a true conditional, if the antecedent is considered to be true (whether or not it actually *is* true), then the consequent must also be true. Like the disjunction, the concept of implication is somewhat ambiguous. Example one above shows that it can apply to the likelihood of behavior. The person is stating the likelihood of his opponent's behavior when certain conditions are met. Some proverbs are of this type: "If a ruler pays attention to lies, all his servants become wicked" (Prov. 29:12). Example two above is a cause/effect relationship. The flipping of the switch causes the diode to light. Example three is an implication by definition; all dogs are mammals. Example four refers to a promise, assuming other conditions are met (if your healing is the Lord's will, for example). Example five refers to a sufficient condition, in this case, the condition for a student's suspension.

Propositional logic deals with this ambiguity by recognizing that each of the given examples are false when the antecedent is true and the consequent is false. If he moves his rook but his opponent does not put him in check, example

ample one is false. If the switch is flipped and the diode doesn't light, example two is false, and so on. All other combinations of true and false in the conditional are considered to be true.

The defining truth table for the conditional is thus:

p	q	$p \supset q$
T	T	T
T	F	F
F	T	T
F	F	T

The last two rows may cause some problems. How can *if FALSE then TRUE* be considered true? Worse yet, how can *if FALSE then FALSE* be true? These are good questions to ask, though the answer may be hard to grasp. But consider the following examples of such propositions:

If *a poodle is a tiger*, then *a poodle is a mammal*.
        F   T

If *a poodle is a tiger*, then *a poodle is a feline*.
        F   F

Both of these conditional propositions are true. If a poodle really was a tiger (i.e. if the antecedent, though false, was *considered* to be true), then a poodle would be a mammal (which of course it is). You see that it is possible for an *if FALSE then TRUE* proposition to be true. Similarly, if a poodle really was a tiger, then it really would be a feline. This *if FALSE then FALSE* proposition is true.

Now, it is equally possible to develop *if FALSE then TRUE* conditionals and *if FALSE then FALSE* conditionals which are false (Try it!). This shows that conditional propositions in English are not really truth-functional when the antecedent is false. However, logicians have agreed that such conditionals should be considered true, which in practice seems to work well.

Another way of thinking about this is to consider $p \supset q$ as meaning $\sim(p \bullet \sim q)$. So the proposition 'If I move my rook then he puts me in check' is considered logically equivalent to 'It is false that I move my rook and he does not put me in check.' Another example: 'If you study then you will pass' is equivalent to 'It is false that you study but you don't pass.' Consider these carefully and you should see the sense in them.

The following truth table development of ~ (p • ~q) shows that it has the same pattern as p ⊃ q:

p	q	~q	(p • ~q)	~ (p • ~q)
T	T	F	F	T
T	F	T	T	F
F	T	F	F	T
F	F	T	F	T

Other equivalent compound propositions could be developed which show this same T F T T pattern, as we shall later see.

Summary: The conditional is an important logical operator. It represents *if/then* propositions and has the symbol ⊃. The conditional is considered false if and only if the antecedent is true and the consequent is false. Thus, p ⊃ q can be considered equivalent to ~ (p • ~q).

Exercise Nine

1.   Develop the truth table for the compound proposition ~p v q on the line below.

p	q	~p	~p v q
T	T		
T	F		
F	T		
F	F		

2.   To what compound proposition is ~p v q equivalent? _____

If A, B and C represent true propositions and X, Y and Z represent false propositions, determine whether the following compound propositions are true or false and circle the appropriate letter.

3.   A ⊃ B   T   F

4.   B ⊃ Z   T   F

5.   X ⊃ C   T   F

6.   (A ⊃ B) ⊃ Z   T   F

7.   X ⊃ (Y ⊃ Z)   T   F

8.   (A ⊃ Y) v (B ⊃ ~C)   T   F

9.   [(X ⊃ Z) ⊃ C] ⊃ Z   T   F

10. [(A • X) ⊃ Y] ⊃ [(X ⊃ ~Z) v (A ⊃ Y)]   T   F

If S represents *I will go swimming* and C represents *The water is cold*, symbolize the following:

11. If the water is not cold then I will go swimming. _____

12. I will go swimming if the water is cold.   _____

The Biconditional

The final logical operator we will consider is the *biconditional*. Biconditionals represent *if and only if* propositions, such as: 'Skyscrapers are buildings if and only if it is false that skyscrapers are not buildings.' The symbol for biconditional is ≡. The previous example could thus be written B ≡ ~ ~B (read as *B if and only if not not B*).

The biconditional can be considered as the conjunction of a conditional and its converse. Taking p ⊃ q as the conditional and q ⊃ p as its converse, this means the p ≡ q is logically equivalent to (p ⊃ q) • (q ⊃ p). You can see why it is called the biconditional. We can use this equivalent proposition to develop the defining truth table for the biconditional:

p	q	p ⊃ q	q ⊃ p	(p ⊃ q) • (q ⊃ p)
T	T	T	T	T
T	F	F	T	F
F	T	T	F	F
F	F	T	T	T

Thus the biconditional is true when both parts are true or when both parts are false. In other words, the biconditional is true if and only if the truth values of both parts are the same.

We can rewrite the defining truth table for the biconditional more simply as:

p	q	p ≡ q
T	T	T
T	F	F
F	T	F
F	F	T

The biconditional has another useful function beyond translating 'if and only if' propositions. Since the biconditional is true whenever the truth values of the component parts are the same, the biconditional can be used to determine whether or not two propositions are **logically equivalent**; that is, it can show if two propositions have identical truth values.

Consider the example from the previous page, in which it was stated B ≡ ~ ~B. The truth table for this is:

B	~B	~ ~B	B ≡ ~ ~B
T	F	T	T
F	T	F	T

This biconditional is always true, so B and ~ ~B are seen to be logically equivalent.

A proposition which is true for every row in the truth table is called a **tautology**. In other words, tautologies are statements which are true by logical structure. The compound proposition B ≡ ~ ~B is thus a tautology. Other important tautologies are p ⊃ p and p v ~p. So we can now say more briefly that the biconditional of logically equivalent propositions is a tautology.

When a proposition is false for every row in the truth table, you have a **self-contradiction**. Self-contradictions are statements which are false by logical structure, such as p • ~p.

Consider the propositions p ⊃ q and p • ~q, along with their biconditional. We will do this truth table (and every one from now on) without guide columns, simply placing the truth values immediately below the variables p and q and working outward, finishing with the ≡.

$$(p \supset q) \equiv (p • ~q)$$

```
T T T   F   T F F T
T F F   F   T T T F
F T T   F   F F F T
F T F   F   F F T F
```

Because the biconditional is a self-contradiction, we can say that p ⊃ q contradicts p • ~q.

Summary: The biconditional represents *if and only if* propositions and has the symbol ≡. The biconditional is true if and only if both parts have the same truth value. When the biconditional of two propositions is a tautology, the propositions are logically equivalent. When it is a self-contradiction, the propositions are contradictory. A tautology is a statement which is true by logical structure. A self-contradiction is a statement which is false by logical structure.

Exercise Ten

Set up the biconditional for each pair of propositions to determine if they are logically equivalent, contradictory, or neither. In this exercise, do not use guide columns. Rather, place the truth values immediately beneath the variables and work outward. Problem 4 will require eight rows.

1. ~(p v q)　　~p v ~q

2. p ⊃ q　　~q ⊃ ~p

3. ~(~p v q)　　p ⊃ q

4. p ⊃ (q ⊃ r)　　(p ⊃ q) ⊃ r

5. Write a set of propositions in English which could be symbolized by problem #2.

Truth Tables for Determining Validity

So far we have seen two purposes which truth tables serve: they are used to determine truth values of compound propositions, and they help define logical operators. Another purpose served by truth tables, and perhaps the most practical (and thus the most interesting), is to determine the validity of propositional arguments.

Before we look at how truth tables do this, we first need to review what is meant by **validity**. When an argument is valid, the conclusion follows necessarily from the premises. In other words, *if the premises are assumed to be true,* then in a valid argument *the conclusion must also be true.* If an argument has true premises with a false conclusion, it is invalid.

To use truth tables to determine the validity of an argument, the argument is translated into symbolic form (if it is not already symbolic) then placed above a line, with the symbol ∴ (meaning *therefore*) in front of the conclusion. Then the truth values are placed below the propositions, just like we have done before. These steps are completed for the *modus ponens* argument shown:

p ⊃ q	p	∴ q
T	T	T
F	T	F
T	F	T
T	F	F

Notice that p and q (and thus p ⊃ q) have the same pattern of T and F that we have seen up to this point.

Now consider again the definition of validity. How does the truth table show that this argument is valid? Well, the argument must be either valid or invalid. If it was invalid, there would be a horizontal row which showed *true premises* with a *false conclusion.* No such row exists; the argument is not invalid. So it must be valid.

Consider this another way. Look at each of the four rows for the above argument. For *every* row in which all the premises show T, does the conclusion also show T? Yes it does; the first row above is the only row with all true premises, and it also shows a true conclusion. The argument is thus valid. If *any* row showed premises with all Ts and a conclusion with F, it would be invalid, even if *other* rows had premises with all Ts and a conclusion with a T.

For an example of an argument shown to be invalid by truth table, consider the *denying the antecedent* argument here:

p ⊃ q	~p	∴ ~q	
T	F	F	
F	F	T	
T	T	F	←INVALID
T	T	T	

The truth values have been completed for the premises and conclusion, with the initial truth values for p and q removed for the sake of clarity. Now, notice that the third row has true premises with a false conclusion. This argument is thus invalid (even though the fourth row shows true premises with a true conclusion). To mark it as invalid, identify the row (or rows) with true premises and a false conclusion and write INVALID near it, as shown above.

Let's look at two more examples of truth tables for validity, one valid and one invalid. On the first one we will show the step-by-step procedure. Consider, just for fun, the argument from the previous page: "The argument must be either valid or invalid. If it is invalid then there will be a row of true premises with a false conclusion. There is no row of true premises with a false conclusion. Therefore the argument is valid." We symbolize this argument as V v I, I ⊃ R, ~R, ∴ V, and complete the truth table. First, write out the argument in symbolic form, placing the truth values under the three constants V, I, and R in the same pattern as we used before:

V v I		I ⊃ R	~R	∴ V
T	T	T		
T	T	F		
T	F	T		
T	F	F		
F	T	T		
F	T	F		
F	F	T		
F	F	F		

From these values, determine the other truth values until the entire argument is completed. You may find it easier to start from the right and work your way left.

V v I	I ⊃ R	~R	∴ V
T T T	T T T	F T	T
T T T	T F F	T F	T
T T F	F T T	F T	T
T T F	F T F	T F	T
F T T	T T T	F T	F
F T T	T F F	T F	F
F F F	F T T	F T	F
F F F	F T F	T F	F

Then the unnecessary columns of T and F may be removed (by erasing or marking out), leaving only the patterns for the premises and the conclusion, as shown:

V v I	I ⊃ R	~R	∴ V	
T	T	F	T	
T	F	T	T	
T	T	F	T	
T	T	T	T	←VALID
T	T	F	F	
T	F	T	F	
F	T	F	F	
F	T	T	F	

The only row with all true premises is the fourth row down, and it also shows a true conclusion. Thus the argument is valid, as marked.

Now for one more example of an invalid argument before we go on to the assignment. "If we stop here then I will be lost. If we stop here then you will be lost. So either I will be lost, or you will." This can be symbolized S ⊃ I, S ⊃ Y, ∴ I v Y.

The truth table can be developed as before (you should do so on your own), resulting in the following patterns:

S ⊃ I	S ⊃ Y	∴ I v Y
T	T	T
T	F	T
F	T	T
F	F	F
T	T	T
T	T	T
T	T	T
T	T	F ← INVALID

Although there are many rows which have true premises with a true conclusion (namely rows one, five, six and seven), the eighth row shows true premises with a false conclusion. Thus the entire argument has been shown to be invalid, and is marked as such.

We have the following procedure for determining the validity of arguments using truth tables.

The Truth Table Method for Validity:
1. Write the argument in symbolic form on a line.
2. Under the variables, place the columns of **T** and **F**.
3. Determine the columns of **T** and **F** for the propositions following the defining truth tables.
4. Remove any unnecessary columns of **T** and **F**, leaving only the columns for the premises and conclusion.
5. Examine the rows. If any row has all true premises with a false conclusion, the argument is invalid. Otherwise it is valid. Mark the row(s) showing valid or invalid.

Exercise Eleven

Determine the truth value for each compound proposition. Assume that propositions A and B are true, X and Y are false, and P and Q are unknown. Circle **T** if the proposition is true, circle **F** if it is false, circle **?** if the truth value cannot be determin + ed. (Hint: There are two of each.)

1.	P v ~P	T F ?
2.	(P ⊃ P) ⊃ ~A	T F ?
3.	(Y ⊃ P) ⊃ Q	T F ?
4.	P ⊃ (X v Y)	T F ?
5.	~Q • [(P v Q) • ~P]	T F ?
6.	~[P v (B • Y)] v [(P v B) • (P v Y)]	T F ?

Use truth tables to determine the validity of the following arguments. Identify them as either VALID or INVALID, and identify the rows which show this.

7.   p v q   ~p   ∴ q   8.   p ⊃ q   ∴ p ⊃ (p • q)

9. p • q   ∴ p v q   10.   p ⊃ ~q   ~q   ∴ p

11. If Jesus was John the Baptist raised from the dead, then He could do miracles. Jesus did miracles, so He was John the Baptist raised from the dead. (**J** means *Jesus was John the Baptist raised from the dead*, **M** means *He could do miracles*.)

12. If Jeff studies then he will get good grades. If Jeff does not study then he will play. So Jeff will either get good grades or he will play. (**S** means *Jeff studies,* **G** means *He will get good grades,* **P** means *He will play.*)

13. If Jesus is not God then He was a liar or He was insane. Jesus was clearly not a liar. He certainly was not insane. We conclude that Jesus is God. (**G** means *Jesus is God,* **L** means *He was a liar,* **I** means *He was insane.*)

14. If taxes increase then the public will complain, but if the deficit increases then the public will complain. Either taxes or the deficit will increase. Thus the public is bound to complain. (**T** means *Taxes increase,* **P** means *The public will complain,* **D** means *The deficit increases.*)

Exercise Twelve

On a *separate sheet of paper,* use truth tables to determine the validity of the propositional arguments below. (Problems four and five require eight rows each, problem six requires sixteen!)

1.   p   ∴ ~p ∨ q

2.   p ⊃ q   ∴ ~q ⊃ ~p

3.   p ⊃ q   ~q   ∴ p ≡ q

4.   p ⊃ (q ⊃ r)   q   ∴ r ⊃ p

5.   p ⊃ (~q ⊃ r)   p   ∴ ~r ⊃ q

6.   (p ⊃ q) • [(p • q) ⊃ r]   p ⊃ (r ⊃ s)   ∴ p ⊃ s

Shorter Truth Tables for Determining Validity

In exercise twelve, you found that you needed to write hundreds of Ts and Fs because of the number of variables. And each time a new variable is added, the size of the truth table doubles. With this level of complexity it is easy to get confused or make careless errors. Surely there must be a shorter method!

Well, there is. All the work in a truth table can (for most arguments) be compressed into only one row. That's right, just one. Here is how it works.

Remember that an argument is proved invalid whenever the premises can be shown to be true and the conclusion false. With the shorter truth table, you start by *assuming the argument to be invalid*. You assume each premise is true and the conclusion is false. Then, you work backwards along the argument, trying to make this assumption work without any contradictions. If you succeed, you have proved the argument to be invalid. However, if assuming the argument to be invalid results in a contradiction, then your assumption is wrong and it must be valid.

Take, for example, one of the arguments from the last chapter. We start by assigning the premises the value T and the conclusion the value F. Notice that the Ts and F are placed under those parts of the propositions which would be filled in last in the longer truth table.

$$S \supset I \qquad S \supset Y \qquad \therefore I \vee Y$$

$$\text{T} \qquad\qquad \text{T} \qquad\qquad \text{F}$$

Now, for the disjunction I v Y to be false as assumed, both disjuncts must be false, according to the defining truth table. But if I and Y are false in the conclusion, they must be false in the premises. Thus we obtain

$$S \supset I \qquad S \supset Y \qquad \therefore I \vee Y$$

$$\text{T F} \qquad\quad \text{T F} \qquad\quad \text{F F F}$$

A true conditional with a false consequent must also have a false antecedent (check the defining truth table for the conditional). Thus we assign the antecedents S in the above conditionals the value of F, as shown:

$$S \supset I \qquad S \supset Y \qquad \therefore I \vee Y$$

F T F	F T F	F F F	INVALID

We are now finished. We assumed the argument was invalid, every truth value was determined, and no contradiction was found. Thus we conclude the argument is indeed invalid.

Now we will look at the valid argument from the last chapter. Again, we start by assuming the argument to be invalid (true premises, false conclusion), then work backward to see if we get a contradiction.

$$V \vee I \qquad I \supset R \qquad \sim R \qquad \therefore V$$

T	T	T	F

If V is false in the conclusion, it must be false everywhere else. Write F under the V in the first premise. Also, if ~R is true, then R must be false. We write F under the Rs and get

$$V \vee I \qquad I \supset R \qquad \sim R \qquad \therefore V$$

F T	T F	T F	F

Now, look at I ⊃ R. For this conditional to be true with a false consequent, the antecedent I must be false. And if I is false there, then it is false in V v I. Filling these in gives us

$$V \vee I \qquad I \supset R \qquad \cdot R \qquad \therefore V$$

F T F	F T F	T F	F	VALID

↖ CONTRADICTION

We see that V and I are both found to be false. But this would imply the disjunction V v I is false. However, we assigned it as a premise the value of true. This contradiction means that it is impossible to make the argument invalid. Thus it must be valid.

Now for two familiar examples. First, consider the *modus tollens* argument p ⊃ q, ~q, ∴ ~p. We will assume it to be invalid, as such:

p ⊃ q	~q	∴ ~p
T	T	F

Start with the conclusion. If ~p is false as assumed, then p is true. Filling that in gives us

p ⊃ q	~q	∴ ~p
T T	T	F T

But if ~q is true, q must be false:

p ⊃ q	~q	∴ ~p
T T F	T F	F T	VALID

↖ CONTRADICTION

We see the contradiction in the first premise, mark it as a contradiction and write VALID.

For a final example, let's look at *affirming the consequent*. We assume it to be invalid:

p ⊃ q	q	∴ p
T	T	F

We see that p is false and q is true, and write those values in.

p ⊃ q	q	∴ p
F T T	T	F	INVALID

There is no contradiction. The argument is invalid, with true premises and a false conclusion.

When a shorter truth table is completed for an invalid argument as above, you should discover that the truth values found for the variables (or constants) are the same truth values from the row showing invalid on the longer truth table. In this case, the argument was seen to be invalid when p is false and q is true. Compare this with the longer truth table:

p ⊃ q	q	∴ p
T	T	T
F	F	T
T	T	F ← INVALID
T	F	F

We see that the longer truth table also shows the argument to be invalid when p is false and q is true.

Thus we have the following procedure for determining the validity of arguments using the shorter truth table:

The Shorter Truth Table Method for Validity:

1. Write the argument in symbolic form on a line.
2. Assume the argument is invalid by assigning the premises the value **T** and the conclusion the value **F**.
3. Work backwards along the argument, determining the remaining truth values to be **T** or **F** as necessary, avoiding contradiction if possible.
4. If the truth values are completed without contradiction, then the argument is invalid as assumed.
5. If a contradiction is unavoidable, then the original assumption was wrong and the argument is valid.

Exercise Thirteen

Determine the validity of the following arguments using the shorter truth-table method. Use the constants given in order of appearance in the argument to symbolize each proposition.

1.   If I study for my test tonight then I am sure to pass it, but if I watch TV then I will get to see my favorite show. So if I study for the test and watch TV, then I will either pass the test or I will see my favorite show. (S, P, W, F)

2.   If Caesar had been a benevolent king, then all Romans would have received their full rights under the law. The Roman Christians were persecuted for their faith. If all Romans had received their full rights, then the Roman Christians would not have been persecuted. Therefore Caesar was not a benevolent king. (B, R, P)

3.   If I promise to feed the dog and bathe it, and if I promise to clean up after the dog's messes, then my mother will let me keep it. If promising to clean up after the dog's messes implies that mother will let me keep the dog, then if I pay for the dog with my own money then I will be allowed to name it myself. I will pay for the dog with my own money. Therefore, if I promise to feed the dog then I will be allowed to name it myself. (F, B, C, K, P, N)

4.   If the book of Hebrews is Scripture then it was written by Paul or Apollos. If Paul wrote anonymously to the Hebrews then he wrote anonymously in some of his letters. If Hebrews was written by Paul then he wrote anonymously to the Hebrews. Paul did not write anonymously in any of his letters. The book of Hebrews is Scripture. Therefore Hebrews was written by Apollos. (S, P, A, H, L)

5.   If you sin apart from the law then you will perish apart from the law, but if you sin under the law then you will be judged by the law. If you sin, then you either sin apart from the law or you sin under the law. You do sin. Therefore you will either perish apart from the law or you will be judged by the law. (A, P, U, J, S)

6.   If you obey the law then you will not be condemned. You have not obeyed the law. You will be condemned. (O, C)

7-12. Determine the validity of the arguments in exercise twelve using the shorter truth-table method.

Using Assumed Truth Values in Shorter Truth Tables

The arguments which have been examined so far have avoided one difficulty which may arise while using the shorter truth-table method. To understand what that difficulty is, consider the following argument: 'It is false that both reading and skiing are dangerous activities. Therefore neither reading nor skiing is dangerous.' This argument follows the form ~ (p • q), ∴ ~ (p v q). If we begin using the shorter truth table to determine validity we get to this point:

$$\underline{\sim (p \bullet q) \qquad \therefore \ \sim (p \vee q)}$$

$$\text{T} \quad \text{F} \qquad\qquad \text{F} \quad \text{T}$$

Now we are stuck. For the conjunction to be false, either p or q could be false, and for the disjunction to be true, either p or q could be true. This situation, in which there are no 'forced' truth values, we must *assume a truth value.* In other words, we need to guess. Looking at the conclusion, we will guess that p is true. Working this out leads us to this:

$$\underline{\sim (p \bullet q) \qquad \therefore \ \sim (p \vee q)}$$

$$\text{T T F F} \qquad\qquad \text{F T T F} \qquad \text{INVALID}$$
$$\diagdown \text{ GUESS}$$

Our guess allowed us to find a way to make the premises true and the conclusion false, and thus determine that the argument is invalid, without having to go any further. In fact, any guess we could have made would have worked with this example. Try another guess before you go on.

Let's look at a different example. Consider this argument:

$$\underline{\text{p} \equiv \text{q} \qquad \text{q} \supset \text{r} \qquad \therefore \text{p} \equiv \text{r}}$$

$$\text{T} \qquad\qquad \text{T} \qquad\qquad \text{F}$$

After taking the first step we are already stuck. There are two ways the biconditional can be true, two ways it can be false, and three ways for the conditional to be true. So we must guess. Like before, we will guess that p is true. Following the procedure leads us to obtain this:

$$p \equiv q \qquad q \supset r \qquad \therefore p \equiv r$$

$$T\;T\;F \qquad\qquad F\;T\;F \qquad\qquad T\;F\;F$$
$$\text{\\ CONTRADICTION} \qquad \text{\\ GUESS}$$

We get a contradiction in the first premise, which appears to imply that the argument is valid. However, it may simply mean that we made a bad assumption. Whenever a contradiction is reached after the first guess, we must then try the other way. So we will now assume that p is false, which leads to us this:

$$p \equiv q \qquad q \supset r \qquad \therefore p \equiv r$$

$$F\;T\;F \qquad\qquad F\;T\;T \qquad\qquad F\;F\;T \qquad \text{INVALID}$$
$$\text{\\ GUESS}$$

This second guess gave us no contradiction. This means that, in fact, the argument *is* invalid. You see the importance of guessing both truth values for the variable if a contradiction is found the first time.

Since both examples in this section were invalid, you may get the mistaken notion that any time you have to guess, the argument is necessarily invalid. This is not true. The first problem in exercise fourteen is valid, yet you must guess both ways to show this.

After some experience with this method, you should find that your guesses become less random and more educated, and that you are able to determine invalid arguments to *be* invalid after the first guess. This may take some careful thought and practice, so don't get discouraged on the way.

Summary: Sometimes when using the shorter truth-table method for validity, no forced truth values occur before you finish. When this happens, you must guess the truth value of one variable or constant, then continue with the same method. If no contradiction appears, the argument is invalid. If a contradiction does appear, you must guess the other truth value for that variable or constant.

Exercise Fourteen

Use the shorter truth-table method to determine the validity of the following arguments. Most of these (but not all) will require you to guess a truth value.

1. p ≡ q   q ≡ r   ∴ p ≡ r

2. p v q   ∴ p • q

3. p ⊃ q   q ≡ r   ∴ p ⊃ r

4. (p ⊃ q) v (r ⊃ s)   p v r   ∴ q v s

5. p v q   ~[q • (r ⊃ p)]   ∴ ~(p ≡ q)

6. p ⊃ (q ⊃ r)   q ⊃ (p ⊃ r)   ∴ (p v q) ⊃ r

Shorter Truth Tables for Consistency

We have seen that the shorter truth table is a powerful tool for quickly determining the validity of even relatively complex arguments. Shorter truth tables may also be used to determine the consistency of sets of propositions and the equivalence of two propositions. Let's look at consistency first.

To say that propositions are **consistent** simply means that they can be true at the same time. Assuming the truth of consistent propositions will result in no logical contradiction.

For example, consider these two propositions. 'It is false that increasing inflation implies a thriving economy.' 'If inflation is not increasing then the economy is not thriving.' Are these propositions consistent? Can they both be true at the same time? How can we use the shorter truth table to find out? Try to answer these questions before you read on.

These two propositions can be abbreviated this way: $\sim(I \supset E)$, $\sim I \supset \sim E$. If they are consistent, then assuming that they are both true should result in no contradiction. So let's do that. As before, the propositions are symbolized and placed above a line. Then below each proposition place a T, implying that both propositions are true, like this:

$$\sim(I \supset E) \qquad \sim I \supset \sim E$$
$$\overline{}$$
$$T \qquad\qquad\qquad T$$

Now, will this assumption run us into a contradiction? To find out, we determine the forced truth values. Since the second proposition is a conditional which can be true for three out of four combinations of true and false, we can't really do anything with it. But if the first proposition is true, then the conditional $I \supset E$ must be false. This would imply that I is true and E is false. Carry these truth values over to the other proposition and continue this procedure, and you should end up with this:

$$\sim(I \supset E) \qquad \sim I \supset \sim E$$
$$\overline{}$$
$$T\ T\ F\ F \qquad\quad F\ T\ T\ T\ F$$

Assuming that the propositions were all true resulted in no contradiction. Thus they are consistent; they can all be true at the same time.

Now, suppose an attorney at first declared, "My client did not take those papers. The secretary took them." Then later he admitted, "It is false that the secretary took the papers if my client did not." Can his statements all be true? Let's find out. These propositions can be symbolized as follows:

$$\frac{\sim C \qquad S \qquad \sim(\sim C \supset S)}{T \qquad\quad T \qquad\quad T}$$

We assume the attorney's propositions are consistent. Does this lead us to a contradiction? Follow the shorter truth table procedure, and you should end up here:

$$\sim C \qquad S \qquad \sim(\sim C \supset S)$$

$$T \qquad\quad T \qquad\quad T\ T\ \ T\ T \qquad \text{INCONSISTENT}$$
$$\nwarrow \text{CONTRADICTION}$$

If $\sim C \supset S$ is true, then the third proposition must be false. Thus they cannot all be true; the propositions are **inconsistent**.

Summary: Propositions are consistent when assuming them all to be true involves no contradiction. Thus the shorter truth table can be used to determine consistency by making this assumption and checking for a contradiction.

Exercise Fifteen

Using the shorter truth-table method, determine the consistency of the following proposition sets. With problems 6 and 7, use the constants given.

1.   p   ~p ⊃ r   2.   ~ ~p   ~p • q
   _____   _____

3.   p ⊃ q   p   ~q   4.   p ∨ q   ~p
   _____   _____

5.   p ≡ q   q ≡ r   p   ~r
   _____

6.   Mr. Copia owns a Porsche and a mansion. *If he doesn't own a mansion then he either owns a Porsche or it's my imagination.* It's your imagination. (P, M, I)

7.   If I learn grammar or logic then I can use rhetoric. *If you can't use rhetoric then you learn grammar and logic.* (G, L, R)

Shorter Truth Tables for Equivalence

The shorter truth table for equivalence works in a similar way as the shorter truth table for validity. In this method, we assume the two propositions are not logically equivalent, then check to see if that assumption runs us into a contradiction or not. If it does not, then our assumption is correct and they are not equivalent. However, if assuming they are not equivalent always results in a contradiction, then they must be equivalent.

Consider these two propositions: 'If salt is dissolved in water then if an egg is placed in the salty water then it will float.' 'If salt is dissolved in water and an egg is placed in it, then the egg will float.' Are they equivalent?

We symbolize the propositions and place them on a line. Then we assume they are not equivalent. How? By assuming one is true and the other false, as such:

$$S \supset (E \supset F) \qquad (S \bullet E) \supset F$$

$$T \qquad\qquad\qquad F$$

Now determine the forced truth values and check for a contradiction. Doing so results in

$$S \supset (E \supset F) \qquad (S \bullet E) \supset F$$

T T T F F   T T T F F
$\nwarrow$ CONTRADICTION

The contradiction seems to imply that our assumption of non-equivalence was wrong. However, we also need to check the other combination of true and false for non-equivalence. That is, we now should assume the first proposition is false and the second is true. Such an assumption leads us to this point:

$$S \supset (E \supset F) \qquad (S \bullet E) \supset F$$

T F T F F   T T T T F
$\nwarrow$ CONTRADICTION

We tried both possibilities for the propositions to not be equivalent: the first true and the second false, and vice versa. Both attempts wound up in a contradiction, so the assumption was wrong and the propositions are equivalent.

For another example, consider these propositions: 'If the lock is broken then the door won't open.' 'The lock is not broken and the door opens.' To determine their equivalence we symbolize them and assume one to be true and the other false. Try to figure out which you should assume true and which false first.

If we first assume that the conditional is false and the conjunction is true, we end up with a contradiction (try it!). However, if we assume the conditional is true and the conjunction false, we can get to this point:

$$L \supset {\sim}O \qquad {\sim}L \bullet O$$
$$\overline{\phantom{L \supset {\sim}O \qquad {\sim}L \bullet O}}$$
$$\text{F T} \quad \text{T F} \qquad \text{T F F F}$$

The truth values are all assigned and there are no contradictions. The conditional is true and the conjunction is false, thus they are not equivalent.

So we have the following procedure for testing the equivalence of two propositions:

The Shorter Truth Table Method for Equivalence:
1. Write the two propositions in symbolic form on a line.
2. Assume the propositions are not equivalent by assigning one to be **T** and the other **F**.
3. If no contadiction occurs, the propositions are not equivalent.
4. If a contradiction is unavoidable, then switch the assigned truth values and try again.
5. If a contradiction is still unavoidable, then they are **equiv**alent. However, if it is possible to avoid a contradiction, the propositions are not equivalent.

Exercise Sixteen

Using the shorter truth-table method, determine the equivalence of each pair of propositions.

1. $\sim(p \bullet q)$ $\sim p \vee \sim q$

2. $p \supset q$ $p \supset (p \bullet q)$

3. $p \vee (p \supset q)$ $q \supset p$

4. p $p \vee (p \bullet q)$

5. If Christ's righteousness is not imputed to you then you are condemned. *Either Christ's righteousness is imputed to you or you are condemned.*

CHALLENGE: Is $[(\sim p \bullet r) \vee (q \bullet r)]$ equivalent to $[(p \supset q) \bullet r]$?

The Dilemma

Any argument presenting two alternatives, either of which when chosen leads to certain conclusions, may be called a **dilemma**. The dilemma is often used to trap an opponent in debate. It is also a common way of thinking when we are trying to decide what course to take between two apparently opposing options.

For example, you might find yourself reasoning like this: 'If I go to college then I can get a good job, but if I go straight into business then I will make money right away. I will either go to college or straight into business, so I will either get a good job or I will make money right away.' This argument follows the general form of a **constructive dilemma**:

$$(p \supset q) \bullet (r \supset s) \qquad p \lor r \qquad \therefore q \lor s$$

A similar type of argument is the **destructive dilemma**, which follow this form:

$$(p \supset q) \bullet (r \supset s) \qquad \sim q \lor \sim s \qquad \therefore \sim p \lor \sim r$$

Here is an example of such a destructive dilemma: 'If something can be done, then it is possible, and if it can be done easily, then it is likely. Faster-than-light travel is either impossible or unlikely, so it either cannot be done, or it cannot be done easily.'

You can see that constructive dilemmas are sort of an extended *modus ponens,* while destructive dilemmas are like *modus tollens.*

We have seen many dilemmas in previous exercises. See if you can find some. Let's look at a few specific types.

In one constructive type, the antecedent of one conditional is the negation of the antecedent of the other:

$$(p \supset q) \bullet (\sim p \supset r) \qquad p \lor \sim p \qquad \therefore q \lor r$$

Because the second premise is a tautology, it is often left unstated. Here is such an argument: 'If you answer a fool according to his folly, then you will be like him. However, if you do not answer a fool according to his folly, then he will be wise in his own eyes. Therefore no matter how you answer a fool you will either be like him or he will be wise in his own eyes.'

In another type of constructive dilemma, the consequent of each conditional is the same, resulting in the following argument:

$$(p \supset q) \bullet (r \supset q) \qquad p \lor r \qquad \therefore q \lor q$$

In this case the conclusion q v q is equivalent to q, and is usually stated that way. For example: 'If Congressman Jones lied about the sale of arms then he should not be re-elected. Neither should he be re-elected if he honestly couldn't remember something so important. He either lied or he couldn't remember, so he should not be re-elected.'

Consider this dilemma: 'If this bill is to become a law then it must pass the congress and the president must sign it. But either it will not make it through congress or the president will not sign it. Therefore this bill will not become a law.' In symbolic form this follows the pattern

$$p \supset (q \bullet r) \qquad \sim q \lor \sim r \qquad \therefore \sim p$$

You can see that this is a destructive dilemma which has the same antecedent p for both conditionals.

The ability to produce a good dilemma is useful in debate, as is the ability to get out of a dilemma being used against you. Using the shorter truth table, we can easily prove these various dilemmas to be valid. How can we avoid the conclusion of a valid argument? One way is to claim that, though valid, the argument is not sound; that is, one or both of the premises is false. Another way is to show that the argument may be used to prove something else.

Facing a dilemma has been picturesquely referred to as being 'impaled on the horns of a dilemma,' as if it were a charging bull. Three main options are usually presented for escaping the horns of a dilemma:

1.   You could *go between the horns,* meaning you could deny the disjunctive premise and provide a third alternative, somewhere in the middle. In the first example, someone could reply, 'The choice isn't between college or a full time business. You could go to college part time and work part time.' The disjunction is charged with being an *either/or* fallacy (i.e. a false dilemma).

2.   You could *grasp it by the horns*. This is done by rejecting one of the conditionals in the conjunctive premise. For example, with the dilemma about the bill above you could reply, 'Even if the president refuses to sign it, the congress could still override his veto with a two-thirds majority.' And if one conjunct is false then the entire conjunction is false.

3.   Finally, you could *rebut the dilemma* with a counter-dilemma. A counter-dilemma which is made up of the same components as the original dilemma is usually the most rhetorically effective. Consider the dilemma about answering a fool. One possible counter-dilemma is, "If you answer a fool according to his folly, then he will not be wise in his own eyes. And if you do not answer a fool according to his folly, then you will not be like him. Therefore he will either not be wise in his own eyes or you will not be like him.' Notice that the counter-dilemma does not claim that the original dilemma is false or invalid. It simply is another way of looking at the facts in order to arrive at a different conclusion.

Let's consider one more example, and see how all three of these methods could be used against it. Suppose your friend complained, 'If I study for the test then I'll miss my favorite show. But if I don't study then I'll fail the test. I will either study or not study, so I'll either miss my favorite show or I'll fail the test.' How could you answer him?

First, you could go between the horns by saying, 'You could study for the test a little while before your show comes on, then study a little before class tomorrow.' Second, you could grasp his dilemma by the horns, saying 'If you don't study you won't necessarily fail, not if you have been paying attention in class.' Third, you could confront him with this counter-dilemma: 'If you study for the test then you will surely pass, and if you don't study then you'll get to see your favorite show. Either you will study or not, so you will either pass the test or you will get to see your favorite show!'

Summary: A dilemma is an argument presenting two alternatives, either of which leads to a conclusion which is usually unpleasant. The two main types of the dilemma are constructive and destructive. There are three means of avoiding being impaled on the horns of a dilemma: go between the horns by denying the disjunction, grasp it by the horns by denying the conjunction, or rebut the dilemma by means of a counter-dilemma.

Exercise Seventeen

Symbolize the dilemma from the middle of the previous page. Then symbolize the counter-dilemma below it. Use shorter truth tables to demonstrate the validity of both arguments.

1. The dilemma: _____

2. The counter-dilemma: _____

Explain how you could deal with each of the following dilemmas, stating which of the three methods you use:

3.   If angels are material, then they cannot all simultaneously fit on the head of a pin. If angels are immaterial, then they can neither dance nor be in contact with the top of a pin. Angels are either material or immaterial. Either way, all the angels that exist cannot simultaneously dance on the head of a pin.

4.   If you sin apart from the law then you will perish apart from the law, but if you sin under the law then you will be judged by the law. You either sin apart from the law or you sin under the law. Therefore you will either perish apart from the law or you will be judged by the law.

5.   If Congressman Jones lied about the sale of arms then he should not be re-elected. Neither should he be re-elected if he honestly couldn't remember something so important. He either lied or he couldn't remember, so he should not be re-elected.

6.   If taxes increase then the public will complain, but if the deficit increases then the public will complain. Either taxes or the deficit will increase. Thus the public is bound to complain.

7.   Modern prophets either prophesy falsely or truly. If they prophesy falsely, they should be rejected, but if truly, their prophecies must be accepted as equal to Scripture. So their words should either be rejected or accepted as equal to Scripture.

8.   If God were perfectly good then He would be willing to prevent evil, and if God were infinitely powerful then He would be able to prevent evil. But God is either unwilling or unable to prevent evil. Therefore He is either not perfectly good or He is not infinitely powerful.

FORMAL PROOFS OF VALIDITY

FORMAL PROOFS OF VALIDITY

The Rules of Inference

Truth tables are able to prove that an argument is invalid or valid. Formal proofs of validity are unable to prove that an argument is invalid. However, properly written they do show the connection between the premises and the conclusion of a valid argument more clearly than does a truth table. They do so by taking the premises of a valid argument and, following certain rules, deduce the conclusion from the premises in a step-by-step proof of validity.

For example, consider this argument which we have seen before: 'If the book of Hebrews is Scripture then it was written by Paul or Apollos. If Paul wrote anonymously to the Hebrews then he wrote anonymously in some of his letters. If Hebrews was written by Paul then he wrote anonymously to the Hebrews. Paul did not write anonymously in any of his letters. The book of Hebrews is Scripture. Therefore Hebrews was written by Apollos.' This argument may be symbolized as follows, each premise given a number and the conclusion placed off to the side:

$$1.\ S \supset (P \lor A)$$
$$2.\ H \supset L$$
$$3.\ P \supset H$$
$$4.\ \sim L$$
$$5.\ S \quad / \therefore A$$

How may we deduce the conclusion from the premises? First, consider premises one and five: $S \supset (P \lor A)$, S. If the constant S is represented by the variable p, and the compound proposition $P \lor A$ is represented by the variable q, these premises can be put into the form $p \supset q$, p. Now, you should recognize these as the premises to Modus Ponens, and thus from these premises we can conclude q, that is, $P \lor A$. In English, we have taken 'If Hebrews is Scripture then it was written by Paul or Apollos; Hebrews is Scripture' and concluded 'Hebrews was written by Paul or Apollos.' In our proof this intermediate conclusion is written on the next line, with the justification written next to it. Included in the justification are the numbers of the premises used in order, and the rule which, using those premises, has this line as the conclusion, as follows:

79

6. P v A   1, 5 M.P.

This says Modus Ponens (M.P.) was used on steps one and five to get P v A.

Now look at premises three and two. What can be concluded from P ⊃ H, H ⊃ L? It should be evident that the conditional P ⊃ L can be concluded. This follows the rule of Hypothetical Syllogism: p ⊃ q, q ⊃ r, ∴ p ⊃ r. Thus we write the next line in our proof:

7. P ⊃ L   3, 2 H.S.

This conclusion says, 'If Hebrews was written by Paul, then he wrote anonymously in some of his letters.' We deduced it from steps three and two, using the Hypothetical Syllogism (H.S.).

We will now use this conclusion, P ⊃ L, along with the proposition in step four, 'Paul did not write anonymously in any of his letters,' ~L. These two premises follow the pattern p ⊃ q, ~q, from which we may conclude ~p using the rule of Modus Tollens. Thus we have deduced 'Hebrews was not written by Paul,' ~P, and write this with the justification on the next line.

8. ~P   7, 4 M.T.

Now back in step 6 we concluded 'Hebrews was written by Paul or Apollos,' P v A, and here we conclude 'Hebrews was not written by Paul,' ~P. From this we deduce 'Hebrews was written by Apollos,' A, using the rule of Disjunctive Syllogism (D.S.): p v q, ~p, ∴ q. We write this as our final step:

9. A   6, 8 D.S.

The entire proof would end up looking like this:

1. S ⊃ (P v A)
2. H ⊃ L
3. P ⊃ H
4. ~L
5. S   / ∴ A
6. P v A   1, 5 M.P.
7. P ⊃ L   3, 2 H.S.
8. ~P   7, 4 M.T.
9. A   6, 8 D.S.
           Q.E.D.

It is customary to end proofs with Q.E.D. This stands for *quod erat demonstrandum*, which is Latin for 'What was to be explained.'

From this proof we have seen the first four of the following **nine rules of inference:**

Modus Ponens (M.P.)	*Modus Tollens* (M.T.)	*Hypothetical Syllogism* (H.S.)
p ⊃ q	p ⊃ q	p ⊃ q
p	~q	q ⊃ r
∴ q	∴ ~p	∴ p ⊃ r

Disjunctive Syllogism (D.S.)	*Constructive Dilemma* (C.D.)	*Conjunction* (Conj.)
p v q	(p ⊃ q) • (r ⊃ s)	p
~p	p v r	q
∴ q	∴ q v s	∴ p • q

Absorption (Abs.)	*Simplification* (Simp.)	*Addition* (Add.)
p ⊃ q	p • q	p
∴ p ⊃ (p • q)	∴ p	∴ p v q

We will now look at examples of proofs which use the last five of these rules.

Consider this rather trivial argument: 'I like coffee and I like tea. Therefore I either like coffee or I like tea.' This can be represented

$$1. \ C • T \quad / \ ∴ C v T$$

This proof will take two more steps. The first will be to use the rule of Simplification on step one, like this:

$$2. \ C \qquad 1 \ \text{Simp.}$$

Simplification always removes the second conjunct in the conjunction (in this case, T). Also, please note that you may not simplify within a proposition; ~(p • q) may not simplify to ~p.

Now we can use the rule of Addition and obtain the desired conclusion:

$$3. \ C v T \qquad 2 \ \text{Add.}$$

Note that the rule of Addition is the only rule which adds a new variable. The formal proof of validity written out in its entirety looks like this:

$$1. \; C \bullet T \quad / \therefore C \lor T$$
$$2. \; C \qquad\quad 1 \; \text{Simp.}$$
$$3. \; C \lor T \qquad 2 \; \text{Add.}$$
$$\text{Q.E.D.}$$

The final example may be difficult to follow, but it will demonstrate many important concepts along with the last three rules of inference. Consider this dilemma: 'If evil men are allowed freedom of speech then evil writings will be produced. If evil men are not allowed freedom of speech then their rights will be violated. Evil men will either be allowed freedom of speech or they will not be. So either evil writings will be produced or evil men will not be allowed freedom of speech and their rights will be violated.' We can symbolize the argument like this:

$$1. \; F \supset W$$
$$2. \; {\sim}F \supset R$$
$$3. \; F \lor {\sim}F \quad / \therefore W \lor ({\sim}F \bullet R)$$

We recognize it as a dilemma, but the conclusion leads us to believe we must first work with the premise in step two. If we use the rule of Absorption, we can obtain the following:

$$4. \; {\sim}F \supset ({\sim}F \bullet R) \qquad\qquad 2 \; \text{Abs.}$$

Now we can set up the first premise of the Constructive Dilemma, which must have the form $(p \supset q) \bullet (r \supset s)$. In our case if we combine step one with step four using Conjunction we will get this:

$$5. \; (F \supset W) \bullet [{\sim}F \supset ({\sim}F \bullet R)] \qquad 1, 4 \; \text{Conj.}$$

Notice that to do this, the p of the conjunction represented the conditional $F \supset W$, and the q represented the compound proposition ${\sim}F \supset ({\sim}F \bullet R)$.

Now we have the propositions we need in order to use the Constructive Dilemma to get our desired conclusion. Look at steps five, $(F \supset W) \bullet [{\sim}F \supset ({\sim}F \bullet R)]$, and three, $F \lor {\sim}F$. This fits the pattern $(p \supset q) \bullet (r \supset s)$, $p \lor r$, and thus we can conclude the following $q \lor s$:

6. W v (~F • R)   5, 3 C.D.

Follow through the variables and the constants or propositions they represent carefully and you will see how this works.

The entire proof can be written out like this. Read this through slowly to make sure you can follow each step:

1. F ⊃ W
2. ~F ⊃ R
3. F v ~F   / ∴ W v (~F • R)
4. ~F ⊃ (~F • R)   2 Abs.
5. (F ⊃ W) • [~F ⊃ (~F • R)]   1, 4 Conj.
6. W v (~F • R)   5, 3 C.D.
                Q.E.D.

Summary: Formal proofs of validity are proofs of valid arguments in which the conclusions are deduced from the premises in a formal, step-by-step procedure. First, each step of the argument is symbolized and numbered. Then, intermediate conclusions are deduced by applying the rules of inference to the previous steps. For each step a justification is given, in which the numbers of the steps used as premises for the rule are placed beside the abbreviation of the rule. This procedure is continued until the desired conclusion is reached. The nine rules of inference are listed in Appendix B.

Exercise Eighteen

Verify the validity of the rules of inference using the shorter truth-table method.

1. *Modus Ponens* (M.P.)   p ⊃ q   p   ∴ q
    _____

2. *Modus Tollens* (M.T.)   p ⊃ q   ~q   ∴ ~p
    _____

3. *Hypothetical Syllogism* (H.S.) p ⊃ q   q ⊃ r   ∴ p ⊃ r
    _____

4. *Disjunctive Syllogism* (D.S.)   p ∨ q   ~p   ∴ q
    _____

5. *Constructive Dilemma* (C.D.)   (p ⊃ q) • (r ⊃ s)   p ∨ r   ∴ q ∨ s
    _____

6. *Absorption* (Abs.)   p ⊃ q   ∴ p ⊃ (p • q)
    _____

7. *Simplification* (Simp.)   p • q   ∴ p
    _____

8. *Addition* (Add.)   p   ∴ p ∨ q
    _____

9. *Conjunction* (Conj.)   p   q   ∴ p • q
    _____

Recognizing the Rules of Inference

From the examples in the last chapter, it should be evident that recognizing the rules of inference used in proofs is not always easy. The premises and conclusions of the rules can be more complex when used in a proof than when they appear simply as a rule. There are a few reasons for this.

First, the variables in the rules of inference can represent very complicated compound propositions. Here is an example of *Modus Ponens* with compound propositions:

$$[(F \supset \sim C) \lor (Q \equiv X)] \supset (\sim E \lor J)$$
$$[(F \supset \sim C) \lor (Q \equiv X)] \quad \therefore \sim E \lor J$$

You may at first have difficulty recognizing that this follows the pattern

$$p \supset q$$
$$p \therefore q$$

Such complicated compound propositions are especially difficult to recognize as premises of rules of inference when they appear in the middle of a longer proof.

Second, variables can represent propositions which are similar (or identical) to those represented by other variables. This occurs for all the rules of inference, but it is perhaps most common with the dilemma. Consider this dilemma:

$$(A \supset B) \bullet (\sim A \supset B)$$
$$A \lor \sim A \quad \therefore B \lor B$$

Compare this with the Constructive Dilemma as it is written in variable form:

$$(p \supset q) \bullet (r \supset s)$$
$$p \lor r \quad \therefore q \lor s$$

You see that p represents A, but r represents $\sim$A. Even more oddly, both q and s represent the constant B. Such similar representations often occurs in proofs, requiring caution for the student.

Finally, recognizing the rules of inference can be difficult when the variables change value from one step to the next. Consider again the proof from the end of the last chapter:

1. F ⊃ W
2. ~F ⊃ R
3. F v ~F   / ∴ W v (~F • R)
4. ~F ⊃ (~F • R)   2 Abs.
5. (F ⊃ W) • [~F ⊃ (~F • R)]   1, 4 Conj.
6. W v (~F • R)   5, 3 C.D.
           Q.E.D.

In each successive step, the variables p and q had the values shown here:

Step	Rule	Value of p	Value of q
4	Abs.	~F	R
5	Conj.	F ⊃ W	~F ⊃ (~F • R)
6	C.D.	F	W

This same difficulty occurs in algebra. In one problem x = 25, in the next problem x = -8.717. In the case of proofs you must take each new step as a new problem, in which the variables can represent something completely different than before.

The best solution to these difficulties is simply practice. Consequently, you will be doing many proofs of validity in the next few chapters. It is the author's belief that such practice will exercise your mind toward abstract thought in a way that almost no other work can.

Summary: Recognizing the rules of inference in formal proofs can be hindered for the following reasons, among others:
1. Single variables can represent very complicated compound propositions;
2. Variables can represent propositions which are similar to those represented by other variables;
3. Variables can change value from one step to the next within the same proof.

Exercise Nineteen

Identify the rule of inference used in each of the following arguments. You may abbreviate.

1. A v B
   ~A
   ∴ B _____

2. X
   X ⊃ Y
   ∴ X • (X ⊃ Y)_____

3. (Q ⊃ R) • (~Q ⊃ T)
   Q v ~Q
   ∴ R v T _____

4. (C ⊃ D) ⊃ E
   C ⊃ D
   ∴ E _____

5. ~U ⊃ (V v X)
   (V v X) ⊃ W
   ∴ ~U ⊃ W _____

6. (F • ~G) ⊃ ~H
   ~ ~H
   ∴ ~(F • ~G) _____

7. (A ⊃ B) • (C ⊃ D)
   ∴ A ⊃ B _____

8. S v T
   ∴ (S v T) v R _____

9. J ⊃ ~K
   ∴ J ⊃ (J • ~K) _____

For the following formal proofs of validity, give the justification for each step.

10. 1. A v B
    2. A ⊃ C
    3. ~C /∴ B
    4. ~A _____
    5. B _____

11. 1. P ⊃ Q
    2. R
    3. P /∴ R • Q
    4. Q _____
    5. R • Q _____

12. 1. ~M ⊃ N
    2. L ⊃ ~M
    3. L /∴ L • N
    4. L ⊃ N _____
    5. L ⊃ (L • N) _____
    6. L • N _____

13. 1. X ⊃ Y
    2. X
    3. W ⊃ Z /∴ Y v Z
    4. (X ⊃ Y) • (W ⊃ Z) _____
    5. X v W _____
    6. Y v Z _____

14. 1. ~F • G
    2. H ⊃ F /∴ ~H v G
    3. ~F _____
    4. ~H _____
    5. ~H v G _____

15. 1. A
    2. ~A /∴ B
    3. A v B _____
    4. B _____

16. 1.   D ⊃ E
     2.   (D • E) ⊃ (F • G)
     3.   D   / ∴ F
     4.   D ⊃ (D • E)   _____
     5.   D ⊃ (F • G)   _____
     6.   F • G   _____
     7.   F   _____

CHALLENGE: Re-write the proof in problem 13 in one less step.

Exercise Twenty

Determine which rule of inference is used in each of the following arguments.

1. If I sin then I will be disciplined for sinning. Therefore if I
   sin then I will both sin and be disciplined for sinning.   _____

2. Jesus is Man. Jesus is God. So Jesus is both Man and God.   _____

3. If Jesus is living then He is my Savior, but if Jesus did not
   rise from the dead then my faith is futile. Either Jesus is living
   or He did not rise from the dead. Thus either Jesus is my
   Savior or my faith is futile.   _____

4. If God gave the law then it should be obeyed. God gave the
   law. We conclude that it should be obeyed.   _____

5. Jesus was either a bad man or He was God. Jesus was not a
   bad man. Therefore He must have been God.   _____

6. Ezekiel and Jeremiah were both prophets. Thus Ezekiel was
   a prophet.   _____

7. If Ruth was a Gentile then Boaz married a Gentile. If Boaz
   married a Gentile then King David was part Gentile. So if
   Ruth was a Gentile then King David was part Gentile.   _____

8. Judas betrayed Christ. So Judas betrayed Christ or he
   killed himself.   _____

9. If you loved God then you would love your neighbor. You
   do not love your neighbor. It is obvious that you do not
   love God.   _____

Use the shorter truth-table method to determine the validity of the following arguments.

10. If God desires every man to be saved then if God's desires are always fulfilled then every man will be saved. Every man will not be saved. Therefore it is false that both God desires every man to be saved and that God's desires are always fulfilled. (D, F, E)

11. If Mary Magdalene was with the women in the tomb then she would have seen a vision of angels. If she saw a vision of angels then she would have told the apostles about a vision of angels. She told the apostles about a vision of angels. Therefore Mary Magdalene saw a vision of angels and she was with the women in the tomb. (W, V, T)

12. If the first-century Christians were taught that Jesus was coming soon, and if the word "coming" means His final coming, and if "soon" means within a century, then the final coming occurred before the end of the second century. The final coming did not occur before the end of the second century. The first century Christians were taught that Jesus was coming soon. Therefore, either the word "coming" does not mean His final coming, or the word "soon" does not mean within a century. (F, C, S, B)

Developing Formal Proofs

You have now seen many examples of formal proofs of validity being developed. Hopefully you are getting a good grasp of the approach to writing such proofs. Before you tackle some on your own, here are a few helpful hints that you should consider.

When faced with a proof, the beginning student often does not know where to start. He may not have a good understanding of what formal proofs are, let alone know how to write one. If you find yourself in this situation, keep in mind that a formal proof of validity is a way of deducing or deriving the conclusion from the premises. It does this by working with the premises using the rules of inference. Each step in a proof uses one or two of the previous steps as premises, which follow the pattern of the premises in one of the rules of inference, to come up with a desired conclusion following the pattern of the conclusion of that rule.

Keep the goal in mind: you are trying to deduce the conclusion. Compare the conclusion with the steps you have written down. Re-write the premises and the conclusion on scratch paper. Ask yourself, 'What is different between the premises and the conclusion? What do I need to do to the premises to get the conclusion?' Consider writing down on scratch paper every possible deduction you can make from the premises, trying to find something which can be used in your proof.

Try pronouncing each step of the proof which you currently have, either in your head or out loud. This might help you recognize a rule. Read $\sim K \supset (P \bullet R)$ as *If not K then P and R*. Then when you read $\sim (P \bullet R)$ as *Not P and R*, you just might recognize the premises of a *Modus Tollens* and correctly conclude $\sim \sim K$.

For some reason, new logic students often do not see the rules of Absorption or Addition when they are needed. If you are stuck, consider whether or not you can use one of these rules. Become familiar with all the rules of inference. Read over them a few times. They are the tools of the art. A good artist is familiar with his paints and his brushes because he constantly uses them, trying new things with them, mixing them in different ways, and so on. A good artist practices. In order to write formal proofs of validity quickly, you must write many formal proofs of validity.

If you are in the middle of a proof and don't know what to try next, check to see if there are any steps you have not yet used. Usually, though by no means always, every step in a proof is used and used once.

Finally, remember that you are exercising your mind. If you get a mental block, go on to a different problem. When you come back to it, you may see a different approach. Your brain is maturing and growing like your muscles mature and grow. Give it time.

Exercise Twenty-one

Provide the justification for each step in the following formal proofs of validity.

1. 1. P v Q
    2. ~P
    3. Q ⊃ R   / ∴ R
    4. Q   _____
    5. R   _____

2. 1. X ⊃ Y
    2. W ⊃ Z
    3. X v W   / ∴ Y v Z
    4. (X ⊃ Y) • (W ⊃ Z)   _____
    5. Y v Z   _____

3. 1. ~A • B
    2. C ⊃ A
    3. C v D   / ∴ D
    4. ~A   _____
    5. ~C   _____
    6. D   _____

4. 1. F ⊃ G
    2. H ⊃ F
    3. ~(H • G)   / ∴ ~H
    4. H ⊃ G   _____
    5. H ⊃ (H • G)   _____
    6. ~H   _____

5. 1. M • L
    2. (M v N) ⊃ P   / ∴ P
    3. M   _____
    4. M v N   _____
    5. P   _____

6. 1. P ⊃ Q
    2. S
    3. Q ⊃ R   / ∴ (P ⊃ R) • S
    4. P ⊃ R   _____
    5. (P ⊃ R) • S   _____

Construct a formal proof for each of the following arguments in the number of steps given.

7. 1. A • B   / ∴ A v B
    2.
    3.

8. 1. C ⊃ D
    2. (C • D) ⊃ E   / ∴ C ⊃ E
    3.
    4.

9. 1. F v G
    2. ~F   / ∴ G • ~F
    3.
    4.

10. 1. (H ⊃ I) • (J ⊃ K)
    2. H   / ∴ I v K
    3.
    4.

11. 1.   M • L
     2.   (M v N) ⊃ O   / ∴ O
     3.
     4.
     5.

12. 1.   P ⊃ Q
     2.   Q ⊃ R
     3.   ~R / ∴ ~P
     4.
     5.

13. 1.   S ⊃ T
     2.   S v U
     3.   ~T / ∴ U • ~S
     4.
     5.
     6.

14. 1.   V ⊃ W
     2.   X ⊃ V
     3.   ~(X • W) / ∴ ~X
     4.
     5.
     6.

15. 1.   Y ⊃ Z
     2.   (Y • Z) ⊃ A
     3.   ~(Y • A) / ∴ ~Y
     4.
     5.
     6.
     7.

16. 1.   B ⊃ C
     2.   D ⊃ E
     3.   D v B
     4.   ~E / ∴ C
     5.
     6.
     7.

Exercise Twenty-two

"The sons of God were either righteous men or they were angels. If they were righteous then they would have pleased God. They did not please God. Thus they must have been angels." (See Genesis 6:1-5) (R, A, P)

1.   Prove the validity of the above argument using the shorter truth-table method.

2.   Write the formal proof of validity.

3.   Re-write the argument and its proof in ordinary English as a dialogue between two people. Imagine that one is trying to convince the other of the truth of the conclusion by stepping him through the formal proof (without mentioning the justification for each step).

The Rules of Replacement

Now that you have written a number of proofs, you may have recognized that not every valid argument can be proved using only the nine rules of inference. Some more tools, namely the rules of replacement, need to be added to your toolbox. With these and the rules of inference, any valid argument can (theoretically, at least) be proved.

The rules of replacement say that certain propositions are equivalent to other propositions and may replace them wherever they occur. For example, in exercise sixteen you proved that $\sim(p \bullet q)$ is logically equivalent to $(\sim p \vee \sim q)$. This says, for instance, that the proposition 'It is false that both amoebae and fungi are animals' is equivalent to the proposition 'Either an amoeba is not an animal or a fungus is not an animal.' This is *De Morgan's Theorem* (De M.), named after the English logician Augustus De Morgan (1806-1871). De Morgan's Theorem also says that $\sim(p \vee q)$ is equivalent to $(\sim p \bullet \sim q)$. You may prove this equivalence on your own.

The second rule of replacement is *Commutation* (Com.), which simply says that $(p \vee q)$ is equivalent to $(q \vee p)$, and that $(p \bullet q)$ is equivalent to $(q \bullet p)$. These are obvious, but very useful. You could not easily write this formal proof without the rule of Commutation:

$$
\begin{array}{lll}
1. & \sim(P \bullet Q) & / \therefore \; \sim Q \vee \sim P \\
2. & \sim(Q \bullet P) & 1 \; \text{Com.} \\
3. & \sim Q \vee \sim P & 2 \; \text{De M.} \\
& \text{Q.E.D.}
\end{array}
$$

This rule is similar to the Commutative Property in algebra, which says that $a + b = b + a$, and $ab = ba$. To help remember the name, think of two people who live in two different cities, each "commuting" to the other person's city to work.

The third rule of replacement is the rule of *Association* (Assoc.), which basically allows us to move parentheses around whenever the logical operators are either both disjunction or conjunction. In symbolic form this rule says that $[(p \vee q) \vee r] \equiv [p \vee (q \vee r)]$ and $[(p \bullet q) \bullet r] \equiv [p \bullet (q \bullet r)]$. Association also has a counterpart in algebra, the Associative Property of Equality, which says that $a + (b + c) = (a + b) + c$, and $a(bc) = (ab)c$.

The fourth rule of replacement also has a counterpart in algebra, the Distributive Property of Equality, which says $a(b + c) = (ab + ac)$. This is the rule of *Distribution* (Dist.), which grants the equivalence of these pairs of propositions:

$$[p \bullet (q \vee r)] \equiv [(p \bullet q) \vee (p \bullet r)]$$
$$[p \vee (q \bullet r)] \equiv [(p \vee q) \bullet (p \vee r)]$$
$$\uparrow \quad \uparrow \qquad\qquad \uparrow \quad \uparrow$$

Because these sets of propositions are so similar, students often confuse them. The way to keep the conjunctions and disjunctions straight is to note that the first conjunction and disjunction (or vice versa) are in the same order on each side of the equivalence sign, as the arrows show.

The fifth rule is the rule of *Double Negation* (D.N.), which says that the negation of a negation of a proposition is equivalent to that proposition, or $\sim\sim p \equiv p$. This was proved in the lesson on the Biconditional.

The sixth rule of replacement is the rule of Transposition (Trans.). This rule says that a conditional is equivalent to its contrapositive, or symbolically, $(p \supset q) \equiv (\sim q \supset \sim p)$. You proved this equivalence in exercise ten. Notice that this rule is not the rule of transpo*rtation*, but the rule of transpo*sition*. Its similarity to Modus Tollens should be evident.

The next two rules have been mentioned before (though not by name) in the definition of their logical operators. They are the rules of *Material Implication* (Impl.) and *Material Equivalence* (Equiv.). The rule of Material Implication states that $(p \supset q) \equiv (\sim p \vee q)$. This is a very useful rule, allowing us to switch between the conditional and the disjunction when necessary. For example, this rule allows us to prove the rule of Modus Ponens:

1. $p \supset q$		
2. p / $\therefore q$		
3. $\sim p \vee q$	1 Impl.	
4. $\sim\sim p$	2 D.N.	
5. q	3, 4 D.S.	

Q.E.D.

Material Equivalence grants that the following pairs of propositions are logically equivalent:

$$(p \equiv q) \equiv [(p \supset q) \bullet (q \supset p)]$$
$$(p \equiv q) \equiv [(p \bullet q) \vee (\sim p \bullet \sim q)]$$

We saw the first of these when we defined the biconditional. The second equivalence is shown here in the longer truth table format (with the truth-value column for p and q left out for clarity):

p ≡ q	(p • q) v (~p • ~q)
T	T T F F F
F	F F F F T
F	F F T F F
T	F T T T T
↑	↑

The ninth rule is *Exportation* (Exp.), which says [(p • q) ⊃ r] ≡ [p ⊃ (q ⊃ r)]. This rule was proved when we introduced the shorter truth table for equivalence. Here is an example of Exportation in the proof of exercise twenty, problem ten:

1. D ⊃ (F ⊃ E)
2. ~E   / ∴ ~(D • F)
3. (D • F) ⊃ E   1 Exp.
4. ~(D • F)   3, 2 M.T.
             Q.E.D.

The tenth and last rule of replacement is usually considered the oddest of the bunch. It is the rule of Tautology (Taut.). It says a proposition is equivalent to the disjunction or conjunction of itself, or symbolically p ≡ (p v p) and p ≡ (p • p).

In anticipation of the question, "When will we ever need to use that?" consider the proof of problem five in exercise seventeen:

1. (L ⊃ ~R) • (C ⊃ ~R)
2. L v C   / ∴ ~R
3. ~R v ~R   1, 2 C.D.
4. ~R   3 Taut.
          Q.E.D.

The rules of replacement, unlike the rules of inference, allow equivalent propositions to replace each other wherever they occur, even if it is in the middle of a larger proposition. This also means that with the rules of replacement you are allowed to go from right to left as well as left to right.

Summary: The following are the rules of replacement (listed with the rules of inference in Appendix B):

De Morgan's Theorems (De M.)	$\sim(p \bullet q) \equiv (\sim p \vee \sim q)$
	$\sim(p \vee q) \equiv (\sim p \bullet \sim q)$
Commutation (Com.)	$(p \vee q) \equiv (q \vee p)$
	$(p \bullet q) \equiv (q \bullet p)$
Association (Assoc.)	$[p \vee (q \vee r)] \equiv [(p \vee q) \vee r]$
	$[p \bullet (q \bullet r)] \equiv [(p \bullet q) \bullet r]$
Distribution (Dist.)	$[p \bullet (q \vee r)] \equiv [(p \bullet q) \vee (p \bullet r)]$
	$[p \vee (q \bullet r)] \equiv [(p \vee q) \bullet (p \vee r)]$
Double Negation (D.N.)	$p \equiv \sim\sim p$
Transposition (Trans.)	$(p \supset q) \equiv (\sim q \supset \sim p)$
Material Implication (Impl.)	$(p \supset q) \equiv (\sim p \vee q)$
Material Equivalence (Equiv.)	$(p \equiv q) \equiv [(p \supset q) \bullet (q \supset p)]$
	$(p \equiv q) \equiv [(p \bullet q) \vee (\sim p \bullet \sim q)]$
Exportation (Exp.)	$[(p \bullet q) \supset r] \equiv [p \supset (q \supset r)]$
Tautology (Taut.)	$p \equiv (p \vee p)$
	$p \equiv (p \bullet p)$

Exercise Twenty-three

Identify the rule of replacement used. Use the abbreviations.

1. A ≡ (A v A)

2. (M • N) ≡ ~ ~ (M • N)

_____   _____

3. [(R ⊃ S) ⊃ T] ≡ [~ (R ⊃ S) v T]   4. (X • Y) ≡ (Y • X)

_____   _____

5. ~ (P • Q) ≡ (~ P v ~ Q)   6. (F ⊃ G) ≡ (~ G ⊃ ~ F)

_____   _____

7. [(B v C) v D] ≡ [B v (C v D)]   8. [J ⊃ (K ⊃ L)] ≡ [(J • K) ⊃ L]

_____   _____

9. [X v (Y • Z)] ≡ [(X v Y) • (X v Z)] 10. (W ≡ V) ≡ [(W ⊃ V) • (V ⊃ W)]

_____   _____

Justify each step for the following proofs of validity.

11. 1. P ⊃ Q   12. 1. (P • Q) ⊃ R
     2. R ⊃ ~Q / ∴ P ⊃ ~R   2. (P ⊃ R) ⊃ S / ∴ Q ⊃ S
     3. ~~Q ⊃ ~R _____   3. (Q • P) ⊃ R   _____
     4. Q ⊃ ~R   _____   4. Q ⊃ (P ⊃ R)   _____
     5. P ⊃ ~R   _____   5. Q ⊃ S   _____

13. 1. (P • Q) ⊃ R   14. 1. P ⊃ ~Q / ∴ ~Q v (Q • ~P)
     2. ~R / ∴ P ⊃ ~Q   2. ~ ~Q ⊃ ~P   _____
     3. ~ (P • Q)   _____   3. Q ⊃ ~P   _____
     4. ~P v ~Q   _____   4. Q ⊃ (Q • ~P)   _____
     5. P ⊃ ~Q   _____   5. ~Q v (Q • ~P)   _____

15. 1. (P v Q) ⊃ (R • S)   16. 1. (P v Q) ⊃ [(R • (S • T)]
     2. ~R / ∴ ~P   2. Q / ∴ R • S
     3. ~R v ~S   _____   3. Q v P
     4. ~ (R • S)   _____   4. P v Q   _____
     5. ~ (P v Q)   _____   5. R • (S • T)   _____
     6. ~P • ~Q   _____   6. (R • S) • T   _____
     7. ~P   _____   7. R • S   _____

17.　1.　(P v ~Q) v R
　　　2.　~P v (Q • ~P)　/ ∴ Q ⊃ R
　　　3.　(~P v Q) • (~P v ~P)　_____
　　　4.　(~P v ~P) • (~P v Q)　_____
　　　5.　~P v ~P　_____
　　　6.　~P　_____
　　　7.　P v (~Q v R)　_____
　　　8.　~Q v R　_____
　　　9.　Q ⊃ R　_____

18.　1.　P • (Q v R)
　　　2.　P ⊃ [Q ⊃ (S • T)]
　　　3.　(P • R) ⊃ ~(S v T)　/ ∴ S ≡ T
　　　4.　(P • Q) ⊃ (S • T)　_____
　　　5.　(P • R) ⊃ (~S • ~T)　_____
　　　6.　[(P • Q) ⊃ (S • T)] • [(P • R) ⊃ (~S • ~T)]　_____
　　　7.　(P • Q) v (P • R)　_____
　　　8.　(S • T) v (~S • ~T)　_____
　　　9.　S ≡ T　_____

Practice with Proofs

Many proofs can be solved with nineteen rules that couldn't be solved with just nine. However, ten more rules do complicate things a bit. Once you learn the rules of calculus you can do more than you could without them, but the problems get more difficult. Having learned to draw with pencil, learning to paint takes more practice. But paints bring in a new beauty that was not possible with pencil alone. Once learned, painting, solving calculus, and solving formal proofs can be an enjoyable challenge. In fact, solving formal proofs is very much like solving puzzles, and can give the same kind of satisfaction.

A similar satisfaction comes in knowing that your reasoning skills are improving. Gaining those skills requires training through guided practice. To assist that training, we will consider some more helpful hints along with more examples of solving proofs. Imagine that you have to prove this argument: 'I either read my Bible and pray or I do not grow in the Lord. If I read my Bible then I will be convicted of sin. Therefore if I am to grow in the Lord then I will be convicted of sin.' This could be symbolized as such:

$$1. (R \bullet P) \lor {\sim}G$$
$$2. R \supset C \quad / \therefore G \supset C$$

What approach can I take to solving this proof?

First, I look at the conclusion and ask, "How can I get that conclusion from those premises?" Well, the constants must come from somewhere. I must get the G from the first premise and the C from the second, since that is where they appear. The conditional must also come from somewhere. If a conditional is in the conclusion like it is here, I will most likely need to use either Hypothetical Syllogism or Material Implication, since these are the only two rules with a simple conditional as a conclusion. Comparing the conclusion with the second premise, I see that if I can get $G \supset R$, then I could use Hypothetical Syllogism with that second premise to get the conclusion. So I must get $G \supset R$ from the first premise.

The first premise is a disjunction. How do I get a conditional like $G \supset R$ from a disjunction like $(R \bullet P) \lor {\sim}G$? Well, looking through the rules I see that Material Implication translates disjunctions into conditionals, because $({\sim}p \lor q) \equiv (p \supset q)$. I first need to put the disjunction in the right order using Commutation, as follows:

3. ~G v (R • P)   1 Com.

If I try Material Implication now, I will get G ⊃ (R • P). But I need G ⊃ R, so how can I drop the P? The only rule that drops constants is Simplification, and I cannot simplify within a proposition. But I note that I have a proposition of the form p v (q • r), so I can use Distribution. Doing so will then allow me to use Simplification, as follows:

4. (~G v R) • (~G v P)   3 Dist.
5. ~G v R   4 Simp.

Again, notice that in order to realize that I could use Simplification, I had to think of the entire proposition (~G v R) • (~G v P) as p • q.

The disjunction ~G v R translates into the G ⊃ R conditional I wanted, which will allow me to finish the proof.

6. G ⊃ R   5 Impl.
7. G ⊃ C   6, 2 H.S.
         Q.E.D.

This proof, like many others, used Material Implication to translate between a conditional and a disjunction. De Morgan's Theorems likewise allow us to translate between conjunctions and disjunctions. Because more rules of inference and replacement are written using conjunctions and disjunctions, you should make sure you are very familiar with the rules of Material Implication and De Morgan's Theorems. You will need them.

With arguments built around a Hypothetical Syllogism where the consequent of the one conditional is worded differently from the antecedent of the other, much of the proof is simply getting the consequent of the first to match the antecedent of the second, as in this argument:

1. A ⊃ (B • C)
2. (B v C) ⊃ D   / ∴ A ⊃ D

The solving of this proof requires seven more steps, all but the last step making the (B • C) match the (B v C). You will solve this in the exercise.

Before we go on to the exercise, however, let me give you some final hints for solving formal proofs:

FORM OF CONCLUSION	CONSIDER TRYING THIS
1. $p \supset q$	Either use H.S., trying to get the consequent of one conditional to match the antecedent of the other, or use Impl., translating between disjunction and conditional.
2. $p \bullet q$	Use Conj., deducing both conjuncts from the premises.
3. $p \lor q$	Either deduce one of the disjuncts from the premises and use Add. to get the other, or use DeM, C.D. or Impl., all of which have disjunctions as conclusions.
4. Constant in conclusion not in premises.	You must use the rule of Addition somewhere in the proof to add that new constant.
5. Conditional in the conclusion not in premises.	You must use the rule of Material Implication somewhere in the proof to translate between a disjunction and a conditional.

In general, look at the conclusion, compare it with the conclusions in the rules of inference and replacement, and figure out how to get the premises of those rules from the premises available in the proof. Keep in mind that you have both the premises and the conclusion to work with. You might find it helpful to work forward from the premises and backward from the conclusion, trying to get them to match somewhere in the middle.

Finally, remember that, though brevity is an admirable goal, there are usually many ways to solve a proof, and a longer method may be perfectly acceptable.

Exercise Twenty-four

Write a formal proof of validity for each of the following arguments.

1. 1. A / ∴ B ⊃ A
    2.
    3.
    4.

2. 1. C ⊃ (D ⊃ E) / ∴ D ⊃ (C ⊃ E)
    2.
    3.
    4.

3. 1. F ⊃ (G • H) / ∴ F ⊃ G
    2.
    3.
    4.
    5.

4. 1. I ⊃ J / ∴ I ⊃ (J v K)
    2.
    3.
    4.
    5.

5. 1. L ⊃ N / ∴ (L • M) ⊃ N
    2.
    3.
    4.
    5.
    6.

6. 1. P ⊃ Q
    2. ~Q / ∴ P ≡ Q
    3.
    4.
    5.
    6.

7. 1. ~R ⊃ (S v T)
    2. ~S
    3. ~T / ∴ R
    4.
    5.
    6.
    7.

8. 1. U ⊃ W
    2. ~(U ⊃ X) / ∴ W
    3.
    4.
    5.
    6.
    7.

9.　1.　A ⊃ (B • C)
　　2.　(B v C) ⊃ D　/ ∴ A ⊃ D
　　3.
　　4.
　　5.
　　6.
　　7.
　　8.
　　9.

10.　1.　E　/ ∴ F ⊃ F (Hint: Use Impl. three
　　2.　　　　　　　　　　　　times)
　　3.
　　4.
　　5.
　　6.
　　7.
　　8.
　　9.

11.　1.　(G v H) ⊃ I
　　2.　(J v K) ⊃ ~I
　　3.　K　/ ∴ ~H
　　4.
　　5.
　　6.
　　7.
　　8.
　　9.
　　10.

12.　1.　(L v M) ⊃ N
　　2.　P ⊃ M
　　3.　~N　/ ∴ ~P • ~L
　　4.
　　5.
　　6.
　　7.
　　8.
　　9.
　　10.

Write out in English an argument (note: not the whole proof) that could be symbolized by the problems identified. Do they sound valid? Why or why not?

13. Problem #1

14. Problem #10

Exercise Twenty-five

Translate the following arguments into symbolic form. Write a formal proof of validity for each. Each proof requires no more than four additional steps.

1.   If evolutionary theory is correct then the biblical creation account is false. However, if the Bible is God's word then the biblical creation account is true. Therefore if evolutionary theory is correct then the Bible is not God's word. (E, C, G)

2.   It is impossible to both spend eternity in heaven and be condemned hell. So if you go to heaven you will not be condemned to hell. (H, C)

3.   If Jesus both helped others and argued rationally then he was not insane. If the gospel accounts are true then Jesus argued rationally and he helped others. Thus either the gospel accounts are false or Jesus was not insane. (H, A, I, G)

4. If God and Satan are both omnipotent then our cosmology is essentially dualistic. God is omnipotent. We must conclude that if Satan is also omnipotent then our cosmology is dualistic. (G, S, D)

5. If the heavens are infinite then I cannot comprehend them, but neither can I comprehend them if they come to an end. If the heavens are not infinite then they come to an end. In any case, I cannot comprehend the heavens. (I, C, E)

6. Either Peter was a liar when he claimed that Jesus never lied, or Jesus never lied. If Peter was a liar when he made this claim then he was a hypocrite. Peter was no hypocrite. Therefore Jesus was no liar. (P, J, H)

The Conditional Proof

Sometimes an argument is intuitively valid, but the proof is still fairly complicated. For example, exercise twenty-four, problem five required the following proof:

$$
\begin{array}{lll}
1. & L \supset N \quad / \therefore (L \bullet M) \supset N & \\
2. & (L \supset N) \lor \sim M & 1 \text{ Add.} \\
3. & \sim M \lor (L \supset N) & 2 \text{ Com.} \\
4. & M \supset (L \supset N) & 3 \text{ Impl.} \\
5. & (M \bullet L) \supset N & 4 \text{ Exp.} \\
6. & (L \bullet M) \supset N & 5 \text{ Com.} \\
& \text{Q.E.D.} &
\end{array}
$$

This solution assumes that the person solving it was able to realize that he could build the proof around the rule of Exportation, not to mention realizing that he had to start by adding ~M. Most people are less creative and would require many more steps to solve this proof. The argument is far more intuitive than the proof. Suppose someone said, 'If you can run a four-minute mile then you are a world-class athlete." The conclusion "If you can run a four-minute mile and you are a woman then you are a world-class athlete" follows rather obviously from that.

Part of the obviousness of this argument results from the fact that the conclusion is a conditional, and we tend to think of conditionals themselves as self-contained arguments. The above argument might be re-worded, "If you can run a four-minute mile then you are a world-class athlete. You can run a four-minute mile and you are a woman. You must be a world-class athlete." This argument would be symbolized and proven as follows:

$$
\begin{array}{lll}
1. & L \supset N & \\
2. & L \bullet M \quad / \therefore N & \\
3. & L & 2 \text{ Simp.} \\
4. & N & 1, 3 \text{ M.P.} \\
& \text{Q.E.D.} &
\end{array}
$$

This argument is much easier to prove. But in order to make it easier we had to change the argument slightly. Rather than do that, we can introduce the **Conditional Proof** (C.P.). Whenever a conditional is used in a proof (such as in the conclusion of the argument), the Conditional Proof allows us to assume the antecedent of the conditional. If from the antecedent we can conclude the consequent, we can then conclude the entire conditional. For our example this would look like

1. L ⊃ N   / ∴ (L • M) ⊃ N
2. L • M   C.P.A.
3. L   2 Simp.
4. N   1, 3 M.P.
5. (L • M) ⊃ N   2-4 C.P.
          Q.E.D.

This proof is still shorter than the original, and much easier to develop once you understand the conditional proof.

Notice how this worked. We saw that the conclusion was a conditional. We assumed the antecedent L • M, and justified it with C.P.A., "*Conditional Proof Assumption.*" We then derived the consequent N. This allowed us to conclude (L • M) ⊃ N in steps 2 through 4 by the Conditional Proof.

We need to consider a few more factors before you can do the exercise. First, you should be aware that the conclusion itself need not be a conditional in order to use the Conditional Proof. All that is necessary is that a conditional is somewhere in the proof, as in this example:

1. [P ⊃ (Q ⊃ P)] ⊃ R   / ∴ R
2. P   C.P.A.
3. P v ~Q   2 Add.
4. ~Q v P   3 Com.
5. Q ⊃ P   4 Impl.
6. P ⊃ (Q ⊃ P)   2-5 C.P.
7. R   1, 6 M.P.
          Q.E.D.

Second, a Conditional Proof Assumption may only be made when using the Conditional Proof. You are not allowed to make an assumption and then use that to derive a conclusion which does not follow from the Conditional Proof. For example, the following proof is not allowable:

    1. P ⊃ Q / ∴ P ∨ R
    2. P   C.P.A.
    3. P ∨ R   2 Add.
          ERROR

Similarly, you may not select one step out of a Conditional Proof to use later on in the proof. We could not do the following:

    1. L ⊃ N / ∴ L • [(L • M) ⊃ N]
    2. L • M   C.P.A.
    3. L   2 Simp.
    4. N   1, 3 M.P.
    5. (L • M) ⊃ N   2-4 C.P.
    6. L • [(L • M) ⊃ N]   3, 5 Conj.
          ERROR

When using any part of the Conditional Proof you must use all of the Conditional Proof.

Summary: The Conditional proof is used when a conditional occurs somewhere in a proof. The antecedent of the conditional is assumed and the consequent derived. The steps involved in this are used to conclude the entire conditional.

Exercise Twenty-six

Write a formal proof of validity for the following arguments using the Conditional Proof.

1. 1. A ⊃ (B • C) / ∴ A ⊃ B   2. 1. D ⊃ E / ∴ D ⊃ (E v F)
    2.   2.
    3.   3.
    4.   4.
    5.   5.

3. 1. G ⊃ H   4. 1. J ⊃ K
    2. G ⊃ I / ∴ G ⊃ (H • I)   2. L ⊃ K / ∴ (J v L) ⊃ K
    3.   3.
    4.   4.
    5.   5.
    6.   6.
    7.   7.

5. 1. M ⊃ N   6. 1. Q ⊃ (R • S)
    2. P ⊃ ~N / ∴ ~M v ~P   2. (R v S) ⊃ T / ∴ Q ⊃ T
    3.   3.
    4.   4.
    5.   5.
    6.   6.
    7.   7.
    8.   8.

7. 1. U / ∴ W ⊃ W   8. 1. X / ∴ Y ⊃ X
    2.   2.
    3.   3.

9.   1.   (A ⊃ B) • (C ⊃ D)   / ∴ (A • C) ⊃ (B • D)
     2.
     3.
     4.
     5.
     6.
     7.
     8.
     9.
     10.
     11.
     12.

CHALLENGE: Solve problem nine without using the Conditional Proof.

Reductio ad Absurdum

The shorter truth-table method for validity is a particular kind of **reductio ad absurdum**, which is Latin for 'bringing to absurdity.' In a reductio ad absurdum, the negation of what we are trying to prove is assumed. If this assumption leads to a contradiction, then it was wrong and we may conclude what we are trying to prove.

The reductio is a common method of proof in mathematics. For example, to prove that division by zero is not allowed, we could assume that division by zero *is* allowed and look for a contradiction. The proof might go like this:

$$0 = 0 \qquad \text{Reflexive property of equality}$$
$$0 \bullet 1 = 0 \bullet 2 \qquad \text{Multiplication property of zero}$$
$$1 \neq 2 \qquad \text{Division by zero}$$

Obviously $1 \neq 2$, so our assumption about the division by zero was false. The reductio can be used in almost any argument or proof. It is in fact a common method in Christian apologetics.

A similar procedure can be used in formal proofs of validity. Suppose that you were asked to prove the rule of Addition without using the rule of Addition. Such a proof is impossible using only the methods of formal proof we have learned so far, because no rule other than Addition allows us to introduce a new variable. However, we could use a reductio ad absurdum, as follows:

1.	P /∴ P v Q	
2.	~(P v Q)	R.A.A.
3.	~P • ~Q	2 De M.
4.	~P	3 Simp.
5.	P • ~P	1, 4 Conj.
6.	P v Q	2-5 R.A.
	Q.E.D.	

We assumed the negation of our conclusion, and justified it with R.A.A. for *Reductio ad Absurdum Assumption*. Then following our regular rules, we tried to obtain a contradiction of the form p • ~p, which we did in step five. The contradiction tells us that our original assumption in step two was wrong, and we thus conclude its opposite in step six. The justification is labelled "2-5 R.A." for

*R*eductio ad *Ab*surdum in steps two through five.

Similar considerations apply to Reductio ad Absurdum as to the Conditional Proof. First, Reductio ad Absurdum may be part of a larger proof. You may negate something other than just the conclusion and use the reductio on that to obtain a different conclusion. Second, the Reductio Assumption may only be made when using Reductio ad Absurdum. Finally, the portion of the proof from the Reductio Assumption to the contradiction must be used collectively; you may not select one step out of a Reductio ad Absurdum to be used later in the proof after the conclusion of the Reductio.

Summary: Reductio ad Absurdum allows us to assume the negation of a conclusion. If that negation leads us to a contradiction of the form p • ~ p, then we may make the original conclusion.

Exercise Twenty-seven

Write a formal proof of validity for the following arguments using Reductio ad Absurdum.

1. 1. ~P ⊃ (Q v R)
    2. ~Q
    3. ~R / ∴ P
    4.
    5.
    6.
    7.
    8.

2. 1. (~P v Q) ⊃ (R • S)
    2. ~R / ∴ P
    3.
    4.
    5.
    6.
    7.
    8.

3. 1. P ⊃ Q
    2. Q v P / ∴ Q
    3.
    4.
    5.
    6.
    7.

4. 1. P / ∴ Q ⊃ Q
    2.
    3.
    4.
    5.
    6.

CHALLENGE: Solve problem three *without* using Reductio ad Absurdum.

Proving Rules Unnecessary

The previous chapter included a proof of the rule of Addition which did not use that rule. This shows that, if other rules remain intact, the rule of Addition is to some degree unnecessary. Every formal proof that uses the rule of Addition could replace that step with the steps from the proof of the rule of Addition. Similar conclusions could be made about each of the other rules of inference. The very reasonable question could be asked, "If we eliminate some unnecessary rules, we would have less rules to memorize; how many rules can we prove unnecessary and yet still have the tools we need to prove any valid argument? "

On the other hand, we should immediately recognize that the more rules we eliminate, the longer our proofs get. A proof which uses Constructive Dilemma, for example, would need to be about nine steps longer if that rule was eliminated. This raises the contrary question, " If doing so would result in shorter proofs, why not add more rules of inference?"

Logicians have tried to strike a happy medium somewhere between the theoretical minimum number of rules and the theoretical minimum average length of proofs. The various authors of logic books have come to different conclusions. Some, for example, include the rule of Destructive Dilemma (see page 72) with the other rules of inference. Others not only leave out this rule, but also leave out the Conditional Proof and Reductio ad Absurdum. The decision concerning which rules to include and which to exclude depends largely upon the author's goals. For example, this textbook includes the Reductio ad Absurdum, not because it is a particularly useful tool (most proofs employing it are no shorter than otherwise), but because this author believes that a good understanding of the reductio technique is useful outside of the realm of formal proofs of validity, such as in mathematics, rhetoric, and apologetics.

The logic student should understand that the number of rules of inference, though not completely arbitrary, is also not absolute. Logicians have been granted some freedom to choose which rules to include based upon their desires and goals, according to the level of wisdom God has given them. The next exercise will give you some opportunities to consider these questions.

Exercise Twenty-eight

This assignment should be done on a separate sheet of paper.

1. Write a formal proof of validity for the Destructive Dilemma. This can be done in two additional steps.

$$(P \supset Q) \bullet (R \supset S)$$
$$\sim Q \vee \sim S \quad \therefore \sim P \vee \sim R$$

2. Invent and name your own rule of inference. Then use that rule to solve a proof from a previous exercise in fewer steps than it was previously solved. Include both proofs for comparison.

3-7. Show the rules Modus Tollens, Absorption, Hypothetical Syllogism, Disjunctive Syllogism, and Addition to be unnecessary by writing formal proofs of validity for them without using those rules anywhere in your proofs. You may use any of the other rules of inference, the rules of replacement, the Conditional proof, and Reductio ad Absurdum.

CHALLENGE: Show Constructive Dilemma to be unnecessary, thus reducing the necessary rules of inference down to only three.

Truth-Functional Completeness

In the last chapter we found that we could reduce the number of rules of inference to be used in proofs, at the cost of increasing the size of most proofs. A similar situation exists with the logical operators. Negation, conjunction, disjunction, conditional, and biconditional can be manipulated such that only two of them are used to do the work of all five, but at the cost of increasing the complexity of most propositions. Let's see how this can be done.

We first write out all the possible combinations of true and false for two variables. This requires sixteen columns of four truth values each, as follows:

1	2	3	4	5	6	7	8
T	T	T	T	T	T	T	T
T	T	T	T	F	F	F	F
T	T	F	F	T	T	F	F
T	F	T	F	T	F	T	F

9	10	11	12	13	14	15	16
F	F	F	F	F	F	F	F
T	T	T	T	F	F	F	F
T	T	F	F	T	T	F	F
T	F	T	F	T	F	T	F

Think back to the truth tables. You should recognize column four as the pattern for the variable p, and column six for the variable q. What other columns do you recognize? You should be able to quickly find the patterns for ~p, ~q, p • q, p v q, p ⊃ q, and p ≡ q.

Having correctly identified those, columns one through eight should be completed except for columns one and three. However, column one should be recognized as a tautology, such as p v ~p. What about column three? There are a few possibilities. Column three could be identified as q ⊃ p, or any equivalent proposition such as ~p ⊃ ~q by transposition, p v ~q by implication and commutation, or ~(~p • q) by implication, commutation, double negation and De Morgan's Theorem. Though any one of these will suffice, for reasons we shall later see we will identify it as p v ~q. Thus we have the following columns identified:

p v ~p	p v q	p v ~q	p	p ⊃ q	q	p ≡ q	p • q
T	T	T	T	T	T	T	T
T	T	T	T	F	F	F	F
T	T	F	F	T	T	F	F
T	F	T	F	T	F	T	F

9	10	~q	12	~p	14	15	16
F	F	F	F	F	F	F	F
T	T	T	T	F	F	F	F
T	T	F	F	T	T	F	F
T	F	T	F	T	F	T	F

Having completed those, we now recognize that, whereas column one is a tautology, column sixteen is a self-contradiction, such as p • ~p, or even ~(p v ~p). This should make us consider: column sixteen is the negation of column one, and columns four and six are the negations of columns thirteen and eleven, respectfully. You may notice that whenever the column numbers add up to seventeen, those two columns are negations of each other. Or considered another way, the bottom row is the reverse of the negation of the top row. This allows us to finish identifying the rest of the columns, as follows:

p v ~p	p v q	p v ~q	p	p ⊃ q	q	p ≡ q	p • q
T	T	T	T	T	T	T	T
T	T	T	T	F	F	F	F
T	T	F	F	T	T	F	F
T	F	T	F	T	F	T	F

~(p • q)	~(p ≡ q)	~q	~(p ⊃ q)	~p	~(p v ~q)	~(p v q)	~(p v ~p)
F	F	F	F	F	F	F	F
T	T	T	T	F	F	F	F
T	T	F	F	T	T	F	F
T	F	T	F	T	F	T	F

We have now discovered propositions by which every possible combination of true and false for two variables is identified. We did this using the five logical operators. This means that those five logical operators are **truth-functionally complete.**

However it was said in the first paragraph that only two logical operators could do the work of all five. In other words, we should be able to discover two logical operators which are in themselves truth-functionally complete. Which two?

One way to answer the question is to determine which logical operators are used most frequently in the system discovered above. If you tally them up, you will find that negation was used twelve times, disjunction was used six times, and conjunction, conditional, and biconditional each were used twice. This implies that negation and disjunction would be the easiest to examine in order to discover whether or not they are truth-functionally complete.

The only rows using logical operators other than negation and disjunction are rows five, seven, eight, nine, ten and twelve. Row five is the conditional p ⊃ q, which can be translated ~p v q by Material Implication. Similarly, row twelve could be changed to ~(~p v q).

Then look at row nine, ~(p • q). Using De Morgan's Theorem on that proposition gives us one which uses negation and disjunction, ~p v ~q. Since row eight is the negation of row nine, we can assume that p • q can be converted into ~(~p v ~q).

This leaves us only rows seven and ten, the propositions using the biconditional. How can we convert p ≡ q into a proposition using negation and disjunction? One method would be to use the rule of Material Equivalence, which tells us that p ≡ q is equivalent to (p • q) v (~p • ~q). All that remains is to translate the conjunctions. This first conjunction was translated in the previous paragraph, and the second can be translated using De Morgan's Theorem. Making these changes, p ≡ q can be converted to ~(~p v ~q) v ~(p v q). Notice that we also could have found this as a disjunction of rows eight and fifteen.

How about ~(p ≡ q)? We could simply negate the proposition just discovered, but that would not give us the simplest solution. Rather, consider the other half of the rule of Material Equivalence. That would lead us to write ~(p ≡ q) as ~[(p ⊃ q) • (q ⊃ p)]. Using De Morgan's Theorem would then give us ~(p ⊃ q) v ~(q ⊃ p). All that remains is to convert the conditionals and rearrange to finish with ~(~p v q) v ~(p v ~q), a disjunction of rows twelve and fourteen.

Thus we have found propositions using only negation and disjunction for every possible combination of true and false for two variables. This means that, together, negation and disjunction are truth-functionally complete. The final result is on the next page. You may check the truth value patterns of any of those propositions by developing the truth table for it.

A Demonstration of The Truth-functional Completeness of Negation and Disjunction

p ∨ ~p	p ∨ q	p ∨ ~q	p	~p ∨ q	q
T	T	T	T	T	T
T	T	T	T	F	F
T	T	F	F	T	T
T	F	T	F	T	F

~(~p ∨ ~q) ∨ ~(p ∨ q)	~(~p ∨ ~q)	~p ∨ ~q
T	T	F
F	F	T
F	F	T
T	F	T

~(~p ∨ q) ∨ ~(p ∨ ~q)	~q	~(~p ∨ q)	~p	~(p ∨ ~q)
F	F	F	F	F
T	T	T	F	F
T	F	F	T	T
F	T	F	T	F

~(p ∨ q)	~(p ∨ ~p)
F	F
F	F
F	F
T	F

We have found that we needed only two logical operators, negation and disjunction, to have a truth-functionally complete set. It is even possible to have only one logical operator which is truth-functionally complete, though it is not to be found among the five standard logical operators.

One such truth-functionally complete logical operator is called NOR, which we will give the symbol ∇. Its defining truth table is

p	q	p ∇ q
T	T	F
T	F	F
F	T	F
F	F	T

The logical operator NOR is capable of producing any possible combination of true or false, though fully demonstrating this would require many pages and very complex propositions. Let it suffice to show how NOR may be used to produce the truth tables for conjunction and disjunction:

p	q	(p ∇ p) ∇ (q ∇ q)	(p ∇ q) ∇ (p ∇ q)
T	T	T	T
T	F	F	T
F	T	F	T
F	F	F	F

Working with truth-functional completeness is a fun challenge, as well as providing good practice with the logical operators, truth tables, and some of the rules of replacement. The ability to translate propositions into propositions using other logical operators is also an essential skill in the logic of digital electronics.

Summary: A given set of logical operators is truth-functionally complete when it is capable of forming propositions for every possible combination of true and false. The set of negation and disjunction are truth-functionally complete. Other truth-functionally complete sets are also possible.

Exercise Twenty-nine

Demonstrate that negation and conjunction together form a truth-functionally complete set. Use the numbers given to write your answers below.

1	2	3	4	5	6	7	8	9	10	11
T	T	T	T	T	T	T	T	F	F	F
T	T	T	T	F	F	F	F	T	T	T
T	T	F	F	T	T	F	F	T	T	F
T	F	T	F	F	T	F	T	T	F	T

12	13	14	15	16
F	F	F	F	F
T	F	F	F	F
F	T	T	F	F
F	T	F	T	F

1. _____   9. _____

2. _____   10. _____

3. _____   11. _____

4. _____   12. _____

5. _____   13. _____

6. _____   14. _____

7. _____   15. _____

8. _____   16. _____

CHALLENGE: Develop a conditional proposition p ⊃ q using only NOR.

TRUTH TREES

TRUTH TREES

Truth Trees for Consistency

The consistency of a set of propositions is a foundational concept in symbolic logic. If you recall, a set of propositions is consistent if the propositions can all be true at the same time. The shorter truth table provided a relatively effortless method for determining the consistency of a set of propositions. With this method we simply wrote the propositions in symbolic form, then assumed that they were consistent. If a contradiction was found, the propositions were inconsistent. Otherwise they were consistent.

Truth trees allow us to determine the consistency of a set of propositions by breaking them down into simple components and looking for contradictions. Like shorter truth tables, truth trees display exactly where the contradiction lies in an inconsistent set, as well as allowing us to easily determine the truth values of the variables or constants for which a set of consistent propositions is consistent. The truth tree is a useful tool in higher-level logic.

We will start with a very basic example. Consider the set { A, ~ B • C }. This could represent the propositions 'I like apples' and 'I don't like bananas but I like carrots.' It should be obvious that these propositions are logically consistent; they could both be true at the same time. Now, what would be the truth values of each of the constants if these propositions were both true? Obviously A would have to be true. For the compound proposition ~ B • C to be true, both ~ B must be true and C must be true. This can be demonstrated by **decomposing** the compound proposition, meaning that we break it down into simple propositions or the negation of simple propositions, which together are called **literals**. Thus we would get something like this:

This is a truth tree:

$$
\begin{array}{l}
A \\
\sim B \bullet C \quad \surd \\
\quad \sim B \\
\quad C
\end{array}
$$

The literals can all be true without contradiction. The set is consistent.

We have just drawn a truth tree by decomposing the set of propositions down to their literals. Once the proposition ~ B • C has been decomposed, it is checked off, and from then on ignored. It has been replaced by its literals. With a consistent set like this, we can **recover the truth values** by assigning true to each literal. For the literals which are negations to be true, their simple propositions must be false. We write out the recovered truth values as such:

A	B	C
T	F	T

The set { A, ~B • C } is seen to be consistent when A is true, B is false and C is true. Had we completed a longer truth table for this set of propositions, we would have found that the original set members would be true on the row with A and C as true and B as false (try it!).

As in the formal proofs of validity, it is customary to number each step in a truth tree and provide its justification. When this is done for the previous example, the final result looks like this:

```
1.    A          SM
2.  ~B • C √      SM              CONSISTENT
3.   ~B          2 •D
4.    C          2 •D          A     B     C
      ○                        ─────────────
                               T     F     T
```

The propositions which were members of the original set are labelled SM for 'Set Member.' Steps three and four are justified with 2 •D (meaning *step two, conjunction decomposition*). The circle underneath the truth tree identifies it as an **open branch**, meaning that all the propositions have been decomposed above the circle and no contradictions between literals exist.

Now consider the set { D • ~E, ~ ~E }. Neither proposition in this set is a literal, so both must be decomposed. First, for ~ ~E to be true, E must be true. Thus ~ ~E decomposes down to E. Then, for the proposition D • ~E to be true, D must be true and ~E must be true. The final truth tree looks like this:

```
1.  D • ~E √     SM
2.    ~ ~E √     SM
3.    E          2 ~ ~D        INCONSISTENT
4.    D          1 •D
5.   ~E          1 •D
      3 × 5
```

Again, the decompositions are justified by the step number and the type of decomposition. The justifications show that step three is derived from a *double-negation decomposition* of step two and steps four and five from a conjunction decomposition of step one. There is a contradiction between the literals on steps three and five because E and ~E cannot both be true. Thus we have a **closed branch** which is labelled 3 × 5 (meaning *step three contradicts step five*), and the truth tree is identified as inconsistent. No truth values can be recovered for inconsistent sets.

Also, notice that every line number with a justification has its proposition checked off.

We have seen how conjunctions and double negations are decomposed down to their literals. Now let's examine the decomposition of disjunctions.

Consider this set of propositions: { F v G, ~F }. Is this set consistent or inconsistent? The proposition ~F is already a literal, so the decomposition of the disjunction F v G is all that remains. When is F v G true? A disjunction is true whenever either disjunct is true. To show this on a truth tree, the disjunction is decomposed by branching each disjunct and putting them on the same line, as shown:

```
1.      F v G √
2.        ~F
                /\
3.      F        G
```

Now that the propositions are all decomposed, consider each branch. For the set to be consistent, either ~F and F would both have to be true, or ~F and G would both have to be true. The first is impossible (it is a contradiction), but the second is possible. Thus we have a consistent set. The final product would look like this:

```
1.      F v G √     SM
2.        ~F        SM                    CONSISTENT
              /\
3.      F        G    1 vD          F          G
       2×3    ○                   ‾‾‾‾‾‾‾‾‾‾‾
                                   F          T
```

Step three is justified as a *disjunction decomposition* of step one. The contradiction between steps two and three is identified on the left branch, but the right branch is labelled as open. If one or more branches is open, the set is consistent. The truth values were recovered from the open branch. They show that the members of the set { F v G, ~F } are true when F is false and G is true.

We will consider two more examples before going on to the exercise. First, let's determine the consistency of this set of proposition forms: { p • ~q, ~p v q }. The truth tree is completed as follows:

```
1.  p • ~q √      SM
2.  ~p v q √      SM
3.     p          1 •D              INCONSISTENT
4.    ~q          1 •D
         /\
5.  ~p    q       2 vD
    3×5  4×5
```

Both branches are closed. Thus it is not possible for propositions of the forms p • ~q and ~p v q to both be true.

For our final example, we will examine the consistency of this set: { p • q, q v ~r }. The truth tree is shown:

```
1.  p • q √       SM
2.  q v ~r √      SM                 CONSISTENT
3.     p          1 •D
4.     q          1 •D         p     q     r
         /\                   ───────────────
5.   q     ~r     2 vD         T     T     F
     ○      ○                  T     T     T
```

Both branches are open. From the right branch we recovered the truth values as shown:

```
 p     q     r
───────────────
 T     T     F
```

On the left branch p and q are true as well. But r does not appear on the left branch. When a proposition does not appear on an open branch like this, the recovered truth values should account for both possible truth values of that proposition. Thus from the left branch we would get p and q as true, and r as true and false, as shown:

p	q	r
T	T	F
T	T	T

Since we already recovered p and q as true and r as false from the right branch, we do not repeat those values in the final answer. Thus the original set of propositions is consistent when the propositions p and q are true, regardless of the truth value of r.

We thus have the following procedure for determining the consistency of a set of propositions using the method of truth trees:

The Truth Tree Method for Consistency
1. Write down the set members on numbered lines, labeling them SM.
2. Continuing to number each step, decompose the compound propositions into literals.
3. Check off each proposition as it is decomposed. Justify each step by stating the line number of proposition along with the decomposition rule used.
4. When the set has been decomposed, examine each branch for contradictions. Branches which show no contradictions are open branches and are marked with a ○. Branches with a contradiction are closed branches, and are marked with an × between the step numbers which show the contradiction.
5. If there is at least one open branch, the set is consistent, and the truth values which show consistency may be recovered.

Exercise Thirty

Using the method of truth trees, determine the consistency of the following sets of propositions. Recover the truth values for all consistent sets.

1. { P, ~Q • R }   2.   { ~ ~P, ~P • Q }

3. { P, ~Q, ~P v ~ ~Q }   4.   { ~P • Q, Q v R }

Decomposition Rules

In using truth trees, we have learned how to decompose double negations, conjunctions, and disjunctions. We must now learn how to decompose their negations, along with conditionals and biconditionals and their negations. In doing so we will derive all the necessary decomposition rules.

First we will determine the decomposition rule for a negated conjunction ~(p • q). For this proposition to be true, the conjunction in parentheses must be false. This is the case when either p is false or q is false, that is, when ~p is true or ~q is true. Thus the negated conjunction decomposes like this:

$$\sim(p \bullet q) \; \checkmark$$

$$\overset{\displaystyle \wedge}{\sim p \qquad \sim q}$$

If the literal on either branch is true, ~(p • q) is true.

How about negated disjunction? For ~(p v q) to be true, p v q must be false. In this case both p and q must be false, or ~p and ~q must both be true. Thus the negated disjunction decomposes like this:

$$\sim(p \text{ v } q) \; \checkmark$$
$$\sim p$$
$$\sim q$$

These two decomposition rules could also have been derived using De Morgan's Theorems.

Before we go on to the others, we will look at two examples using these rules. First, we will determine the consistency of the set { ~(P • Q), ~(P v Q) }. The truth tree works out like this:

1.	~(P • Q) √	SM			
2.	~(P v Q) √	SM		CONSISTENT	
3.	~P	2 ~vD			
4.	~Q	2 ~vD		P	Q
5.	~P ~Q	1 ~•D		F	F

The justification for steps three and four would be read *step two, negated disjunction decomposition*. For step five the justification is *step one, negated conjunction decomposition*.

Now for a more complex truth tree. Is the set { ~(~P • Q), ~(P v ~R), Q v R } consistent? For what truth values? One possible truth tree looks like this:

```
1.      ~(~P • Q) √            SM
2.      ~(P v ~R) √            SM
3.      Q v R √                SM
4.        ~P                   2 ~vD            CONSISTENT
5.        ~~R √                2 ~vD
6.         R                   5 ~~D          P    Q    R
              /\                               ─────────────
7.   ~~P √       ~Q            1 ~•D          F    F    T
8.     P           /\          7 ~~D
    4×8          /    \
9.              Q      R       3 vD
             7×9    ○
```

Notice that, as in steps eight and nine, after a branch is closed, you do not continue to branch off of it. Also note in steps five through eight that you are not allowed to 'skip' any double negations. These must be done explicitly.

Now for the last four decomposition rules. First, look at the defining truth table for the conditional:

p	q	$p \supset q$
T	T	T
T	F	F
F	T	T
F	F	T

Because there are three ways for the conditional to be true, you may think that it decomposes into three branches. However, note that $p \supset q$ is true whenever either p is false or q is true. This means that the conditional decomposition needs only two branches, like this:

$$p \supset q \ \checkmark$$

$$\diagup\diagdown$$

$$\sim p \qquad q$$

This decomposition could also have been derived from the rule of Material Implication, which says that $(p \supset q) \equiv (\sim p \lor q)$.

Now look at the defining truth table for the biconditional:

p	*q*	*p* ≡ *q*
T	T	T
T	F	F
F	T	F
F	F	T

For $p \equiv q$ to be true, either p and q must both be true, or p and q must both be false. Or, using the rule of Material Equivalence, we know that $(p \equiv q) \equiv [(p \bullet q) \lor (\sim p \bullet \sim q)]$. Thus the biconditional decomposition is

$$p \equiv q \ \checkmark$$

$$\diagup\diagdown$$

$$\begin{array}{cc} p & \sim p \\ q & \sim q \end{array}$$

For the negated conditional $\sim(p \supset q)$ to be true, the conditional $p \supset q$ must be false. This is only the case when p is true and q is false. Thus the negated conditional decomposition is

$$\sim(p \supset q) \ \checkmark$$
$$p$$
$$\sim q$$

The only situation in which $\sim(p \supset q)$ is true is when both p and $\sim q$ are true.

Finally, consider the truth table for the negated biconditional:

p	q	~ (p ≡ q)
T	T	F
T	F	T
F	T	T
F	F	F

Since ~(p ≡ q) is true when either p is true and q is false or vice versa, the negated biconditional decomposition rule is

$$\sim (p \equiv q) \; \checkmark$$

$$\begin{array}{cc} p & \sim p \\ \sim q & q \end{array}$$

Now we will consider some examples which use these rules. We will first determine the consistency of this set of propositions: { ~(P ⊃ Q), Q ⊃ P }. One truth tree for this set is

```
1. ~(P ⊃ Q) √      SM
2.  Q ⊃ P √        SM              CONSISTENT
3.    P            1 ~⊃D
4.    ~Q           1 ~⊃D            P     Q
       /\
5.  ~Q    P        2 ⊃D             T     F
    O     O
```

You may have noticed that, whenever possible, the propositions which do not branch are decomposed first, as in the example above. This helps prevent the truth tree from being needlessly complicated. However, had we decomposed the second proposition first, we would have obtained the same result.

One final example before the exercise, this time giving us practice with the biconditionals. Determine the consistency of this set of propositions: { ~(P ≡ Q), Q ≡ R, ~P }. The truth tree can be drawn as shown on the next page.

```
 1.   ~(P ≡ Q)√              SM
 2.    Q ≡ R √              SM
 3.       ~P               SM              CONSISTENT
              /\
 4.   P        ~P           1 ~≡D           P     Q     R
 5.  ~Q        Q            1 ~≡D          ─────────────────
       3×4       /\                         F     T     T
 6.         Q      ~Q       2 ≡D
 7.         R      ~R       2 ≡D
            ○      5×6
```

We chose to decompose ~(P ≡ Q) first because this allowed us to immediately close a branch after step five. You may again check to see that the original propositions are all true when the constants have the recovered truth values.

Summary: A truth tree decomposition rule can be developed for any compound proposition. To do so, the necessary truth values for the variables or constants must be determined such that the proposition is true. This has been done for conjunction, disjunction, conditional, biconditional, their negations, and double negation. The decomposition rules are listed in Appendix C.

Exercise Thirty-one

Using the method of truth trees, determine the consistency of the following sets of propositions. Recover the truth values for all consistent sets.

1. { A ⊃ B, A, ~B }

2.   { ~C, ~(C ⊃ D) }

3. { E ⊃ ~F, ~E • F }

4.   { G ≡ H, ~H, G }

5. { J ⊃ ~(J ≡ K), ~(J ⊃ K) }

6. { L ⊃ M, M ⊃ L, ~(L ≡ M) }

Techniques for Constructing Truth Trees

As sets of propositions grow larger, truth trees grow more complex. While constructing them, it helps to have a few basic techniques in mind to assure that they are as uncomplicated as possible.

1. *Decompose non-branching members first*

This technique will save you unnecessary re-writing. For example, compare the two different truth trees below for this set of propositions: { P ≡ Q, Q • R }.

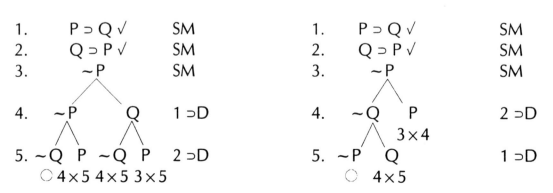

Though they are the same number of steps, the truth tree on the left requires the writing of more constants. This can lead to unnecessary complexity and errors, especially for larger truth trees.

2. *Decompose members which result in the closing of one or more branches*

As we have seen, once a branch in a truth tree is closed, no more branching can occur off of it. Thus, the sooner we can close a branch, the less complicated the truth tree. Compare these two truth trees for the propositions { P ⊃ Q, Q ⊃ P, ~P }.

Decomposing the second proposition first saved us the drawing of two branches, two literals, and one contradiction. You can see how this technique can help in preventing truth trees from becoming bushes!

3. *Stop when the truth tree answers the question being asked*

This may seem to be a rather obvious rule—why do more work than necessary? However, drawing a truth tree can be so absorbing that you might easily keep going after getting the information you need. Say, for example, that you were asked to determine the consistency of this set: { P v Q, ~Q • R, ~R }. You might draw the tree like this:

```
1.     P v Q √            SM
2.    ~Q • R √            SM
3.      ~R               SM
4.      ~Q               2 •D
5.       R               2 •D          INCONSISTENT
          /\
6.   P        Q          1 vD
   3×5      4×6
```

The answer is correct, but the truth tree could have been terminated after step five, due to the contradiction between steps three and five. There was really no good reason for decomposing the disjunction.

Similarly, suppose you were asked to determine the consistency of this set of propositions: { P • Q, Q • R, ~R }. If the propositions were decomposed in the order given, the truth tree would be seven steps long. However, starting with the second proposition results in a tree with only five steps, since there is no need to continue after the contradiction has been reached:

```
1.     P • Q             SM
2.     Q • R √           SM
3.      ~R               SM
4.       Q               2 •D          INCONSISTENT
5.       R               2 •D
       3×5
```

4. *Decompose more complex propositions first*

This technique is included last because it should only be employed when the first three rules do not apply. Decomposing the more complex propositions (like the biconditionals) first may save you from unnecessarily re-drawing a complicated decomposition on unclosed branches. Such is the case with this set of propositions: { ~P, P ⊃ R, ~(~Q ≡ R) }. When decomposed in the order given, the truth tree is:

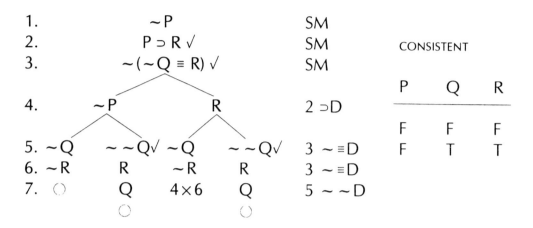

However, if we decompose the negated biconditional first, we obtain this truth tree:

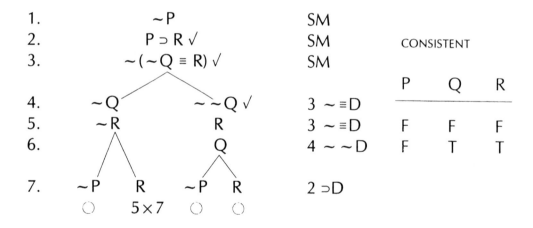

The results are the same, but this second truth tree is clearly less complex than the first. Also, note that more branches result in wider truth trees. Be sure to give yourself plenty of room at the start.

Let's do one more example, keeping these principles in mind. To determine the consistency of the set of propositions { P ≡ (Q v R), ~(Q • R), ~(Q ⊃ ~P) }, the simplest truth tree is

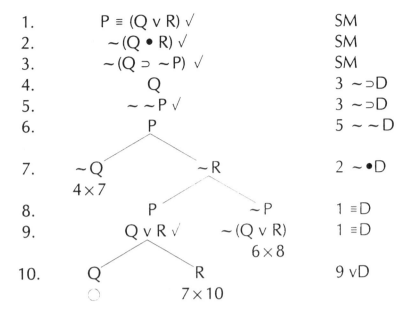

Though this may look somewhat complicated, notice that each new step requires at most one branching. Had the propositions been decomposed in the original order (ignoring the techniques of this lesson), the truth tree would have been far more involved.

Summary: In order to keep truth trees as simple as possible, a few techniques may be employed: Decompose non-branching members, and members which result in the closing of branches, first; Stop when the truth tree yields the required result; If these are not applicable, decompose more complex propositions first.

Exercise Thirty-two

Using the method of truth trees, determine the consistency of the following sets of propositions. Recover the truth values for all consistent sets.

1. { A ⊃ B, (A • B) ⊃ C, ~(A • C), A }   (Hint: Each step need not have
                                                                      more than one branch)

2. { D ≡ (E ⊃ F), ~D • E, D ≡ F }

3. { G ⊃ H, G v I, ~H, ~(I • ~G) }

4. { ~(J ≡ K), K ⊃ (~L v M), L • ~(K • M) }   (Hint: Give yourself plenty of room)

Truth Trees for Self-Contradiction and Tautology

Self-contradiction

Truth trees show that propositions are inconsistent when every branch of the truth tree closes due to contradictions on each branch. This same concept carries over into self-contradictions within a single proposition. If a self-contradiction is decomposed on a truth tree, every branch will close. If they did not, then there would be a way for the proposition to be true, which of course is impossible with a self-contradiction.

This can clearly be seen in the simple self-contradiction P • ~P, which decomposes as such (note that, for the sake of simplicity, the line numbers and justifications were disregarded):

$$P • \sim P \checkmark$$
$$P$$
$$\sim P$$
$$\times$$

Now consider a somewhat larger self-contradiction: ~{[P ⊃ (P • ~Q)] v Q}. The decomposition of this proposition shows a closed tree as well:

1.	~{[P ⊃ (P • ~Q)] v Q} √	SM
2.	~[P ⊃ (P • ~Q] √	1 ~vD
3.	~Q	1 ~vD
4.	P	2 ~⊃D
5.	~(P • ~Q) v	2 ~⊃D
6.	~P ~~Q √	5 ~•D
7.	4×6 Q	6 ~~D
	3×7	

Tautology

As we recognized in the lesson on truth-functional completeness, a self-contradiction is the negation of a tautology. Thus, if we negate a tautology, its decomposition should act like the decomposition of a self-contradiction. That is, the truth tree of the negation of a tautology will have no open branches.

Consider the tautology P v ~P. The decomposition of its negation is as follows:

$$\sim (P \lor \sim P) \ \surd$$
$$\sim P$$
$$\sim \sim P \ \surd$$
$$P$$
$$\times$$

The negation of the proposition gave us a closed truth tree, so the proposition is a tautology.

Note that if we had decomposed the proposition itself, we would have obtained this tree:

$$P \lor \sim P \ \surd$$

$$P \qquad \sim P$$

This is an open tree. You may think that a tree which shows all open branches like this must be the decomposition of a tautology, and so we don't need to negate the proposition and look for closed branches, as we did in the example at the top of this page. But this is not true. Consider this very similar decomposition:

$$P \lor \sim Q \ \surd$$

$$P \qquad \sim Q$$

The proposition is certainly not a tautology, but the truth tree is completely open. The truth tree for the negation of this proposition is also open (try it!). Thus to test for a tautology we must negate the proposition and look for a closed truth tree.

Summary: Truth trees may be used to determine if a compound proposition is a tautology or a self-contradiction. A proposition is a self-contradiction if and only if its decomposition results in a closed tree. It is a tautology if and only if the decomposition of its negation is a closed tree.

Exercise Thirty-three

FOR THIS EXERCISE YOU MAY OMIT LINE NUMBERS AND JUSTIFICATIONS

Decompose each of the following compound propositions to determine if it is a *self-contradiction*. Write YES if it is and NO if it is not.

1. ~P • (P • Q)   2.   P • ~(P • Q)

3. (P ⊃ P) ⊃ (Q • ~Q)   4.   (P • Q) ≡ ~(P v Q)

Decompose the negation of each of the following compound propositions to determine if it is a *tautology*. Write YES if it is and NO if it is not.

1.   ~ (P v Q) ⊃ ~ (P • Q)

2.   ~ (P • Q) ⊃ ~ (P v Q)

3.   (P ⊃ Q) v (Q ⊃ P)

4.   ~ (P • ~Q) ≡ (Q v ~P)

Truth Trees for Equivalence

When two propositions are equivalent, their biconditional is a tautology. Symbolically, because p is equivalent to itself, p ≡ p is a tautology. Thus, if we decompose the negation of this biconditional, we should get a closed truth tree, as we learned in the last lesson. The decomposition is shown here:

$$\sim (p \equiv p) \; \checkmark$$

$$
\begin{array}{cc}
p & \sim p \\
\sim p & p \\
\times & \times \\
\end{array}
$$

This implies that, in general, we can determine the equivalence of any two propositions by decomposing the negation of their biconditional. If we get a closed truth tree, the propositions are equivalent.

Let's use this to show the equivalence of P ⊃ Q and ~ P v Q. The truth tree would be

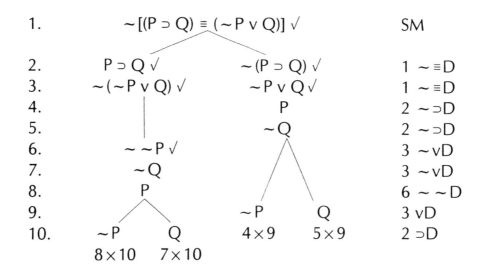

Every branch closed. Thus the biconditional is a tautology, which implies that the two propositions are equivalent.

For comparison, let's do a truth tree for two propositions which are *not* equivalent. We have seen a number of times that ~ (P • Q) is not equivalent to ~P • ~Q. The truth tree which demonstrates this is shown:

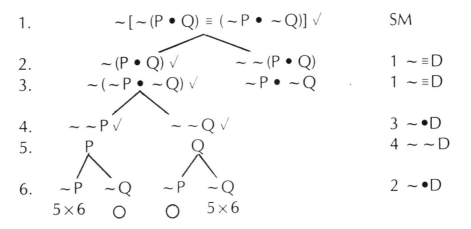

1.	~[~(P • Q) ≡ (~P • ~Q)] √	SM
2.	~(P • Q) √ ~ ~(P • Q)	1 ~ ≡ D
3.	~(~P • ~Q) √ ~P • ~Q	1 ~ ≡ D
4.	~ ~P √ ~ ~Q √	3 ~ • D
5.	P Q	4 ~ ~ D
6.	~P ~Q ~P ~Q	2 ~ • D
	5×6 O O 5×6	

We need not decompose the right hand side, since we have already found open branches on the left. The open branch shows that the negated biconditional can be true, implying that the biconditional is false. This means that the propositions are not equivalent.

Summary: Truth trees may be used to determine the equivalence of two propositions. The propositions are put into a biconditional which is negated. This negated biconditional is then decomposed. The propositions are equivalent if and only if the result is a closed truth tree.

Exercise Thirty-four

Decompose the negation of the biconditional of the two propositions to determine if they are equivalent. Write YES if they are and NO if they are not. Include line numbers and justifications, and recover at least one set of truth values which show non-equivalence.

1. P   P v (P • Q)   2.   P   P • (P v Q)

3. P ⊃ Q   Q ⊃ P   4.   P ⊃ Q   ~Q ⊃ ~P

Truth Trees for Validity

So far we have found that truth trees are able to help us determine the consistency and equivalence of propositions, and to determine if a given proposition is a self-contradiction or a tautology. In this last lesson we shall see how truth trees may be used to determine the validity of arguments.

Recall once again the definition of validity. An argument is valid if and only if the premises necessarily imply the conclusion; if the premises are assumed to be true, then the conclusion must be true. If it is possible for the premises to be true and the conclusion to be false, the argument is necessarily invalid.

Recall also what truth trees do: truth trees demonstrate whether propositions in a set can all be true. If they can all be true, at least one branch of the truth tree is open. If the truth tree is completely closed, the propositions cannot all be true.

Now, how can we use these two concepts to develop a method to determine validity of arguments? We do so in a way very similar to the shorter truth tables; we assume the argument is invalid, then see if that results in contradictions. In other words, we do a *reductio ad absurdum* on the argument.

To assume that the argument is invalid, we simply assume that the premises are true and that the negation of the conclusion is true - that is, that the conclusion is false. Then we decompose these propositions (the premises and the negated conclusion) in a truth tree. If this leads us to contradictions in every way—that is, if the truth tree closes—then the assumption was wrong and the argument is valid. However, if we get an open truth tree, the truth values on the open branch will be those by which the propositions (the premises and the negated conclusion) can be true.

We will use the *modus ponens* argument p ⊃ q, p, ∴ q as an example. We assume that the argument is invalid, that the premises are true and the negation of the conclusion is true. Then we do a truth tree as follows to see if these assumptions are consistent (the premises are labeled P and the conclusion is labeled NC for negated conclusion):

```
1.      p ⊃ q √            P
2.        p                P
3.        ~q               NC
              /\
4.      ~p      q          1 ⊃D
      2 × 4   3 × 4
```

We see that, when we assume the premises are true and the conclusion is false, we end up with contradictions on every branch of the truth tree. This means that our assumption was wrong and the argument is therefore valid.

Now consider the invalid argument of *denying the antecedent*: p ⊃ q, q, ∴ p. We write the premises and the negation of the conclusion as set members, then decompose them in the truth tree as shown:

1.	p ⊃ q √	P
2.	q	P
3.	~p	NC
4.	~p q	1 ⊃D

We see that the set is consistent; it is possible for the premises and the negated conclusion to be true. The recovered truth values are:

p	q
F	T

With these truth value assignments, the premises p ⊃ q and q are true, and the conclusion p is false. Note that p as false and q as true are the same truth values by which the longer truth table shows this argument to be invalid:

p ⊃ q	q	∴ p	
T	T	T	
F	F	T	
T	T	F	←INVALID
T	F	F	

Now for some slightly more complex examples. Consider this argument from exercise twelve: p ⊃ q, ~q, ∴ p ≡ q. We put the premises and the negation of the conclusion in a set and decompose them in a truth tree, as shown on the next page.

1.	$p \supset q$ ✓			P
2.	$\sim q$			P
3.	$\sim (p \equiv q)$ ✓			NC

$$
\begin{array}{ccc}
4. & \sim p & q & \quad 1 \supset D \\
 & & 2 \times 4 & \\
5. & p \quad \sim p & & 3 \sim \equiv D \\
6. & \sim q \quad q & & 3 \sim \equiv D \\
 & 4 \times 5 \quad 2 \times 6 & & \text{VALID}
\end{array}
$$

Assuming the argument to be invalid resulted in nothing but contradictions. So the argument is valid.

For the final example we will look at the argument in the last problem from exercise fourteen: $p \supset (q \supset r)$, $q \supset (p \supset r)$, $\therefore (p \lor q) \supset r$. We do the same procedure as before, resulting in the truth tree shown:

1.	$p \supset (q \supset r)$ ✓	P
2.	$q \supset (p \supset r)$ ✓	P
3.	$\sim [(p \lor q) \supset r]$ ✓	NC
4.	$p \lor q$ ✓	$3 \sim \supset D$
5.	$\sim r$	$3 \sim \supset D$

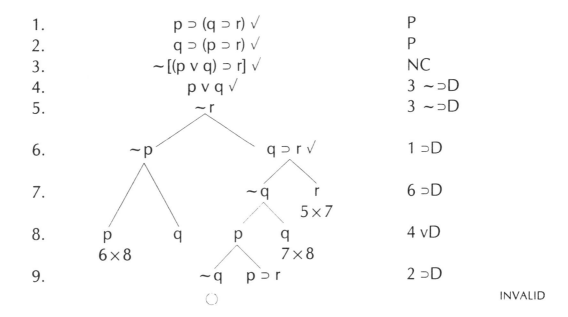

6.	$\sim p$	$q \supset r$ ✓	$1 \supset D$
7.		$\sim q$	r	$6 \supset D$
		5×7	
8.	p	q	p	q	$4 \lor D$
	6×8			7×8	
9.		$\sim q$	$p \supset r$	$2 \supset D$

INVALID

In step nine we find an open branch (with fully decomposed propositions and no contradictions above it). Without going any further we know that there exists at least one possible way to make the premises true and the conclusion false, and thus the argument is invalid. We can recover the truth values which demonstrate the invalidity:

p	q	r
T	F	F

Had we continued the truth tree, we could have recovered more truth values which would demonstrate invalidity, but these are sufficient. You should check to see that, if you assign these truth values to the variables in the original argument, the premises come out to be true and the conclusion false.

Summary: Truth trees can be used to determine the validity of arguments. The set members are the premises and the negation of the conclusion. These members are then decomposed in a truth tree. If the truth tree closes, the argument is valid. If the truth tree has at least one open branch, the argument is invalid and the truth values may be recovered which demonstrate the invalidity of the argument.

Exercise Thirty-five

Use truth trees to determine the validity of the following arguments. If an argument is found to be invalid, recover at least one set of truth values which demonstrate the invalidity.

1. A ⊃ B   B ⊃ C   ~C   ∴ ~A

2. D ⊃ E   F ⊃ E   ∴ D ∨ F

3. (G • H) ⊃ I   H   ∴ G ⊃ I

4.   If an axe was found in the safe then the butler put it there. If the butler put it there then he was guilty of the crime. If he was guilty of the crime then he would be distressed. He was not distressed. Either an axe was found in the safe or the safe was empty. Therefore the safe was empty. (A, B, C, D, E)

5.   If you studied logic then if you did not learn logic then you will not know how to do this problem. If you did not learn logic but you are brilliant then you will know how to do this problem. You know how to do this problem. Thus you either studied logic or you are brilliant (S, L, K, B).

APPENDICES

Appendix A

The defining truth tables for the five logical operators

Negation			Conjunction				Disjunction		
p	$\sim p$		p	q	$p \bullet q$		p	q	$p \vee q$
T	F		T	T	T		T	T	T
F	T		T	F	F		T	F	T
			F	T	F		F	T	T
			F	F	F		F	F	F

Conditional				Biconditional		
p	q	$p \supset q$		p	q	$p \equiv q$
T	T	T		T	T	T
T	F	F		T	F	F
F	T	T		F	T	F
F	F	T		F	F	T

Appendix B

The rules of inference and replacement

1. Modus Ponens (M.P.)   2. Modus Tollens (M.T.)   3. Hypothetical Syllogism (H.S.)
   p ⊃ q   p ⊃ q   p ⊃ q
   p   ~q   q ⊃ r
   ∴ q   ∴ ~p   ∴ p ⊃ r

4. Disjunctive Syllogism (D.S.)   5. Conjunction (Conj.)   6. Constructive Dilemma (C.D.)
   p ∨ q   p   (p ⊃ q) • (r ⊃ s)
   ~p   q   p ∨ r
   ∴ q   ∴ p • q   ∴ q ∨ s

7. Simplification (Simp.)   8. Absorption (Abs.)   9. Addition (Add.)
   p • q   p ⊃ q   p
   ∴ p   ∴ p ⊃ (p • q)   ∴ p ∨ q

Any of the following logically equivalent expressions can replace each other wherever they occur:

10. DeMorgan's Theorems (De M.)

~(p • q) ≡ (~p ∨ ~q)
~(p ∨ q) ≡ (~p • ~q)

11. Commutation (Com.)

(p ∨ q) ≡ (q ∨ p)
(p • q) ≡ (q • p)

12. Association (Assoc.)

[p ∨ (q ∨ r)] ≡ [(p ∨ q) ∨ r]
[p • (q • r)] ≡ [(p • q) • r]

13. Distribution (Dist.)

[p • (q ∨ r)] ≡ [(p • q) ∨ (p • r)]
[p ∨ (q • r)] ≡ [(p ∨ q) • (p ∨ r)]

14. Double Negation (D.N.)

p ≡ ~~p

15. Transposition (Trans.)

(p ⊃ q) ≡ (~q ⊃ ~p)

16. Material Implication (Impl.)

(p ⊃ q) ≡ (~p ∨ q)

17. Material Equivalence (Equiv.)

(p ≡ q) ≡ [(p ⊃ q) • (q ⊃ p)]
(p ≡ q) ≡ [(p • q) ∨ (~p • ~q)]

18. Exportation (Exp.)

[(p • q) ⊃ r] ≡ [p ⊃ (q ⊃ r)]

19. Tautology (Taut.)

p ≡ (p ∨ p)
p ≡ (p • p)

Appendix C

Truth tree decomposition rules

Double negation

$\sim\sim p$ ✓
p

Conjunction

$p \bullet q$ ✓
p
q

Disjunction

$p \vee q$ ✓
p $\quad$ q

Conditional

$p \supset q$ ✓
$\sim p$ $\quad$ q

Negated Conjunction

$\sim(p \bullet q)$ ✓
$\sim p$ $\quad$ $\sim q$

Negated Disjunction

$\sim(p \vee q)$ ✓
$\sim p$
$\sim q$

Negated Conditional

$\sim(p \supset q)$ ✓
p
$\sim q$

Biconditional

$p \equiv q$ ✓
p $\quad$ $\sim p$
q $\quad$ $\sim q$

Negated Biconditional

$\sim(p \equiv q)$ ✓
p $\quad$ $\sim p$
$\sim q$ $\quad$ q